THE
HORSE

THE BRITISH HORSE SOCIETY

THE MANUAL OF
STABLE MANAGEMENT

COMPILED BY
Pat Smallwood FBHS

THE ADVISORY PANEL INCLUDED
Stewart Hastie MRCVS
Jeremy Houghton-Brown
A.J. Lord
Tessa Martin-Bird FBHS
Barbara Slane Fleming FBHS
Helen Webber FBHS

SERIES EDITOR
Jane Kidd
First Published 1988
Reprinted 1990
Reprinted in enlarged format 1991, 1992

© British Horse Society 1988

**British Library Cataloguing in Publication
Data**
British Horse Society manual of stable
  management
  Bk.1: The horse
  1. Livestock: Horses. Management
  I. British Horse Society, *Advisory Panel*
  636.1'083

Produced for The British Horse Society by
The Kenilworth Press Limited,
Addington, Buckingham, MK18 2JR

Printed and bound in Great Britain by
Hollen Street Press Ltd, Slough, Berks.

CONTENTS

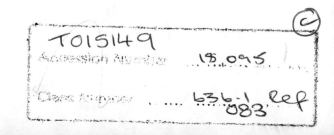

Introduction

The aim of this six-volume series is to provide a reliable source of information and advice on all practical aspects of horse and stable management. Throughout the series emphasis is placed on the adoption of correct and safe procedures for the welfare of all who come into contact with horses, as well for the animals themselves.

The books have been compiled by a panel of experts, each drawing on considerable experience and contributing specialised knowledge on his or her chosen subject.

The other titles in the series are:

Book 2, Care of the Horse—Handling the Horse; Stable Vices and Problem Behaviour; Grooming; Bedding; Clipping, Trimming, Pulling and Plaiting; Recognising Good Health and Caring for the Sick Horse; Internal Parasites; Shoeing.

Book 3, The Horse at Grass—Grassland Management; Management of Horses and Ponies at Grass; Working the Grass-kept Pony or Horse; Bringing a Horse up from Grass.

Book 4, Saddlery—Saddles; Bridles; Other Saddlery; Bits; Boots and Bandages; Clothing; Care and Cleaning of Leather; Saddling and Unsaddling.

Book 5, Specialist Care of the Competition Horse—Dressage Horse; Driving Horse; Show Jumper; Event Horse; Long Distance Horse; Hunter; Show Horse or Pony; Point to Pointer; Polo Pony; Types of Transportation; Travelling.

Book 6, The Stable Yard—Construction; Riding Schools; Organising and Running a Yard; The Buying of Fodder and Bedding; The Law.

NOTE: *Throughout the book the term 'horses' is used and it will often include ponies.*

CHAPTER 1
Conformation

The conformation of a horse or pony affects his soundness, ability to perform and comfort as a ride.

If the horse is in good condition, the following features should be sought:

General Impression
The general impression should be that he is built in proportion, with all sectors matching and his outlook alert, bold and confident. The 'top line' – the neck, withers, back, loins and dock – should form a succession of well-developed outlines, each of which blends smoothly into the other. He should have a good sloping shoulder, a relatively short back and a long croup: i.e. length from hip to point of buttock, giving an appearance of 'standing over a lot of ground', whilst being well balanced over his legs, which are four square under him.

If the horse is in poor condition, only an experienced person with a 'good eye' can assess his potential. It takes skill to recognise whether he has the right make and shape: that when given suitable care, food and work, he will make up into a worthwhile or even top-class animal.

Similarly, too much fat can disguise a horse's out-

The points of the horse.

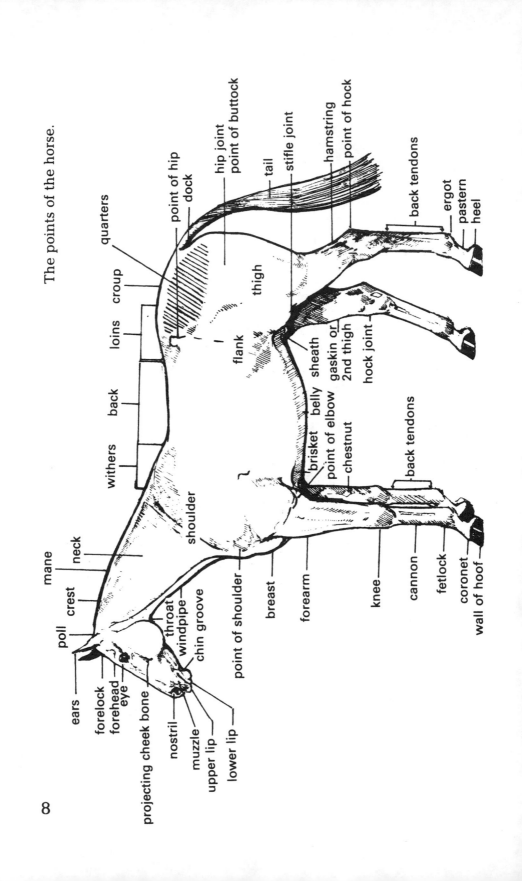

8

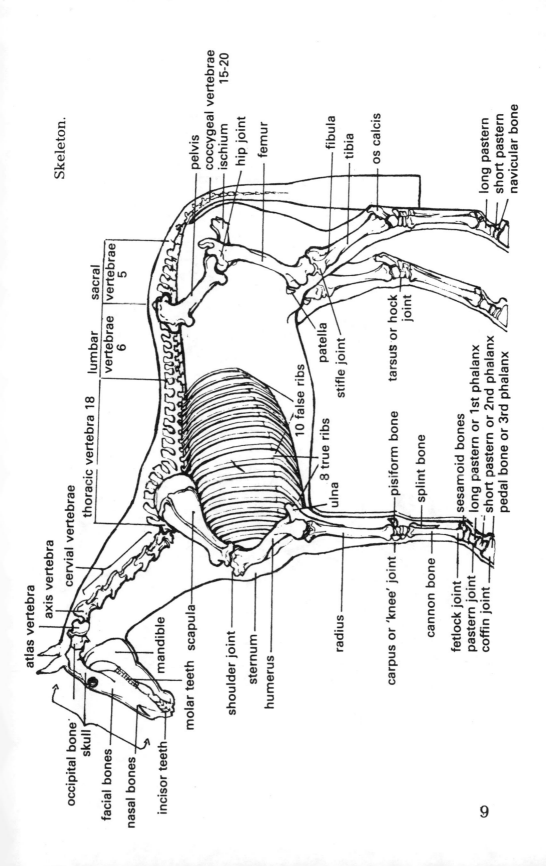

Skeleton.

atlas vertebra
axis vertebra
cervial vertebra
thoracic vertebra 18
lumbar vertebrae 6
sacral vertebrae 5
pelvis
coccygeal vertebrae 15-20
ischium
hip joint
femur
fibula
tibia
os calcis
long pastern
short pastern
navicular bone

occipital bone
skull
facial bones
nasal bones
incisor teeth
molar teeth
mandible
scapula
shoulder joint
sternum
humerus
radius
carpus or 'knee' joint
pisiform bone
splint bone
cannon bone
fetlock joint
pastern joint
coffin joint
sesamoid bones
long pastern or 1st phalanx
short pastern or 2nd phalanx
pedal bone or 3rd phalanx
ulna
8 true ribs
10 false ribs
patella
stifle joint
tarsus or hock joint

9

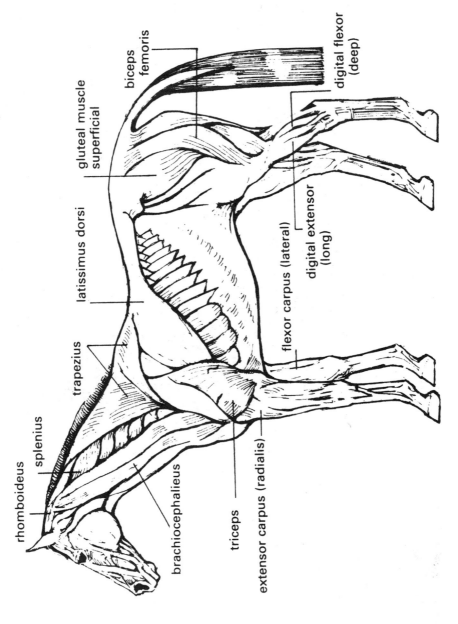

Main superficial external muscles.

- rhomboideus
- splenius
- trapezius
- latissimus dorsi
- gluteal muscle superficial
- biceps femoris
- digital flexor (deep)
- digital extensor (long)
- flexor carpus (lateral)
- extensor carpus (radialis)
- triceps
- brachiocephalieus

line, and can make it difficult to visualise what he will be like when the excess weight is lost and he is fit.

A horse with good skeletal structure, but poor muscle development, can be transformed by being given suitable work and the opportunity to use and develop his muscles in the correct way.

Feet

The much-quoted saying 'no foot no horse' is very true. The make and shape of feet are vital to the soundness and functioning of the horse.

Front feet and hind feet should be matching pairs. Any difference in outline, angle of foot to the ground, or size of frog, should be viewed with suspicion. The only exception is the horse whose foot has been worn down through losing a shoe.

☐ The front feet should slope at an angle of 45 to 50 degrees from the ground.

☐ The hoof wall should continue at the same angle as the pastern.

☐ The hind feet should have slightly more slope, and should be longer and narrower than the front feet.

☐ All feet should point straight forwards. Any deviation from this is caused by poor conformation of the leg, and will result in faulty action.

The heels should be wide, with a well-developed frog to help absorb concussion. The sole should be slightly concave. Contracted heels and poorly developed frogs restrict the blood supply to the foot, and increase the vulnerability to navicular.

Large flat feet can cause problems, particularly on stony ground. They are liable to develop corns and are easily bruised.

Small feet are a disadvantage, as they give a smaller weight-bearing surface, and there is a greater tendency towards unsoundness in the foot.

The wall of the foot should be smooth and free from cracks. Rings and grooves are a sign of change of management or diet; pronounced rings can signify laminitis (see *Shoeing*).

The texture of the horn is of importance. Some breeds of horses have naturally hard feet, especially native ponies, Arabs and Hackneys. Poor horn texture can be improved by careful feeding, particularly the use of the additive Biotin, and by the use of horn stimulants.

A skilled farrier can greatly improve a horse's feet through regular attention. Equally, lack of care or an inexperienced farrier can spoil good feet.

Head
The head should be lean, well set on to the neck, and in proportion to the size of the horse. There should be sufficient width between the branches of the lower jaw to allow ample room for the top of the windpipe. The jaw bone itself should not be too large. There must be room between the lower edge of the jaw bone and the jugular furrow, to allow the horse to flex.

This set of the head on the neck is very important, as it affects respiration, and the ease of flexion, which in its turn affects the control and balance of the horse.

Eyes
The eyes should be of a good size and expression, and widely set to give broad vision. Their expression

is a key to temperament and reliability, and should be bold and generous, not mean and sharp, if the horse is to work well.

Muzzle

The muzzle should be fine with a well-defined nostril. The jaws should be of equal length. If overshot ('parrot mouthed') or undershot, the horse may have problems when biting grass, although his ability to chew will not be affected.

Ears

The ears should be relaxed, mobile and of a good size. When pricked, they should be carried forward. Lop ears droop forwards and down, or to the side and down, but they have no ill effects other than to give an impression of dejection.

Neck

The neck should be muscular and of a length and substance proportional to the body. The top line should be convex, with a definite arch between the withers and poll. A heavy crest, expected in a stallion, is to be regretted in a mare or gelding. The muscle under the neck should appear to slip into the shoulder without any definite division. The neck should not be set into the shoulder so low that there is a big dip between it and the withers.

Neck muscles and thus outline can be improved by correct training.

Shoulder

The shoulder should be deep with a definite slope forward from the withers to its point. This shape gives a better ride, and longer, more flowing strides.

Conformation

The top of the shoulder blades should be close together; if wide apart they make a lump or 'loaded shoulder', which gives an uncomfortable ride and poor movement. Upright shoulders allow the saddle to slip forward, make the rider feel that he has little in front of him, and restrict the freedom of movement of the horse. This type of shoulder is more suitable for the harness horse, as it provides greater pulling power.

Withers

The withers should be clearly defined and of a sufficient height to provide room for the attachment of the covering muscles of the shoulders. If too high, they will make it difficult to fit a saddle, if too low the saddle tends to work forward – which may result in girth galls.

In a mature horse, the withers and croup should be of a similar height. If the croup is higher, the horse appears to be standing downhill, and tends to be on his forehand when ridden. There are, however, some good jumpers and racehorses with this conformation.

Chest

The chest should be of medium width, giving plenty of heart room. If too narrow, the horse moves very close in front with the likelihood of brushing. If too wide, he tends to roll in canter and have limited ability to gallop.

Forelegs

The forelegs positioning will depend on the length of the humerus bone, lying between the elbow and the point of shoulder. If this is too long, the legs are too far

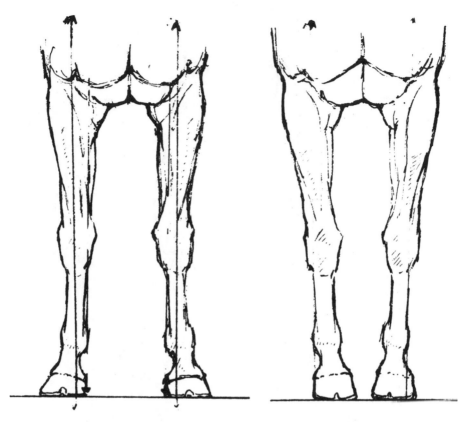

Splayed feet.   Toed in.

under the body, and the elbow is likely to be tied in with a consequent lack of freedom of movement. The elbow should stand well away from the ribs.

The forelegs should be straight from the top of the leg to the foot when looked at from the front, and straight from the top of the leg to the front of the fetlock when looked at from the side. Any deviation from a straight line when looked at from the front is a serious fault, which affects the straightness of the action and gives extra strain on the tendons, ligaments and joints.

The forearm should be well developed, and longer

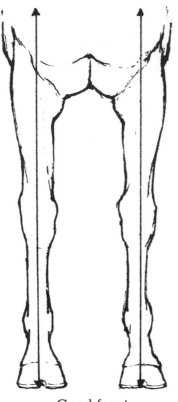 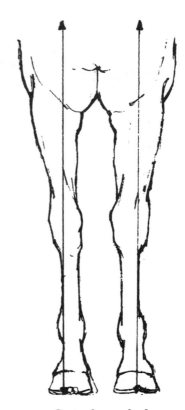

Good front. Out of one hole.

than the leg below the knee which should be relatively short, so as to minimise strain on the ligaments and tendons.

Knees
The knees should be broad, flat and deep to give room for the tendons which are attached over the top of the knee, and also to give room for the attachment of tendons and ligaments at the back of the knee. A well-developed trapezium bone is of help.

A horse 'back at the knee' (concave when viewed from the side) or 'calf kneed' will be suitable for

16

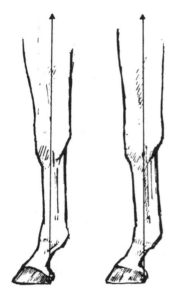
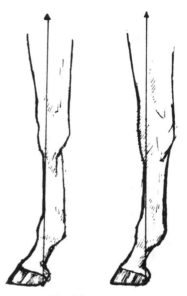

Good knees.   Bad knees.

slower work, but is more likely to strain tendons when galloping and jumping.

A horse a little 'over at the knee' (convex when viewed from the side) is less likely to sprain tendons. This conformation, in many people's opinion, is no drawback. Swollen knees caused by injury are always suspect, and the cause should be investigated.

Cannon Bones

The cannon bones should be short and straight. If narrower below the knee than at the fetlock, the horse is said to be 'tied in below the knee'. There is less room for tendons and ligaments, and therefore a greater risk of strain.

Bone is measured immediately below the knee and is the circumference of the leg at that point. By placing the thumb and first finger round the leg an approximate measurement can be taken: 20cms

(8ins) is sufficient bone for a riding horse or light-weight hunter, although this will depend on breeding; 21.75cms (8½ins) for a medium weight hunter and 23-23.8cms (9-9½ins) for a heavyweight hunter. A well-known saying is that 'blood carries weight'. Thoroughbred and Arab horses have much denser bone structure than a horse of common breeding: i.e. of cart-horse blood. Horses with this denser bone are capable of carrying more weight, relative to their size, than the commoner breeds.

Fetlock
The fetlock joint should give an appearance of flatness rather than roundness. Lumps on the front or the back of the joint are a sign of work and age; if they are on the inside they indicate that the horse moves close and brushes.

Pasterns
Pasterns should be of medium length. Long sloping pasterns make for a springy ride, but are liable to strain. Short, upright pasterns are strong, but give a bumpy ride, and tend to cause lameness through the extra jar and concussion.

Body
The body should be deep through the heart, with well-sprung ribs and plenty of room for the lungs. This gives a natural girth line.

A horse who is shallow through the heart is described as 'showing a lot of daylight' or 'on the leg'. The measurement from the lowest part of the girth to the withers should approximately equal that from the girth to the ground. Many young horses have a 'leggy' appearance, but lose this look as they mature.

Ribs
There are eight true ribs attached to both the vertebrae and the sternum, and ten false ribs attached to the vertebrae at the top and at the bottom, interconnected by cartilage. The first rib is only slightly curved, the curvature of each succeeding rib gradually increasing to give a well-rounded appearance and internal space for many of the main organs of the body.

An animal which is flat sided, which runs up light, and which is 'herring gutted', is usually a 'poor doer', lacking in stamina. There should be only a short gap between the last rib and the point of hip: i.e. 5-8cms (2-3ins).

Back
The back, having to carry the weight, should be of medium length and almost level. Long backs give a comfortable ride but are liable to strain. It is usual for mares to be longer in the back than stallions or geldings. Short backs are strong, but give a less comfortable ride.

Hollow backs are a sign of weakness in young horses, but are also a sign of age in an older horse. Weak or dip-backed horses are often suffering from progressive arthritis.

Roach backs – i.e. arched upwards – are strong but give an uncomfortable ride. This outline can develop with age, and may then signify arthritis.

The correct muscular development of the back and loins area is essential if the horse is to perform well under the weight of the rider.

Loins

The loins are immediately behind the saddle and on either side of the spinal processes. They should be broad and well developed. Their strength and correct muscular development play a major part in the horse's balance and ability to perform. A slack loin goes with a weak back and should be avoided.

Quarters

The quarters provide power and should be muscular, the hips broad, rounded and a pair. 'Hip down' (a fracture of the point of the hip caused by a fall or hitting a door post) is shown by the flatter outline of the injured hip. It can be unsightly but often goes unobserved, and once the initial bruising has subsided, it rarely causes lameness. It can sometimes cause problems in pregnancy. A 'goose-rumped' horse has quarters which slope sharply from croup to dock, and this often accompanies jumping ability. A prominence on the croup is called a 'jumping bump'.

The dock should not be set on too low. There should be plenty of length between the hip and the point of buttock and the point of the hip and point of hock. Viewed from behind, the impression should be one of strength, with rounded quarters and upper or first thighs sloping down to a well-developed second thigh or gaskin. 'Split up behind' means a poorly developed upper thigh.

Hind Legs

When the horse is standing naturally and the hind leg is viewed both from the side and from immediately behind, there should be a straight line from the point of buttock through the point of hock down to the fetlock and so to the ground. Any deviation from this shows a weakness, and places greater strain both on the stifle joint, or the patella above, and the hock joint below it. These two joints of the stifle and hock work in harmony, and provide the main propelling force for galloping and jumping. When in movement, the stifle joint should not be thrown outwards, but should stay in line with the body. The stifle joint is the equivalent of the human knee.

Hocks
The hocks should be large, and the outline should be clean and flat with a prominent point at the back. There should be plenty of bone below the hock. There should be length from hip to hock. The hock should be 'well let down': i.e. the section of the limb from hock to fetlock should appear short.

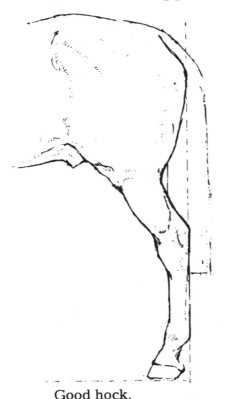

Good hock.   Sickle hock.

Conformation

There are various weak shapes of hock:

Bent or Sickle Hocks.   If viewed from the side, there is a more acute angle to the hocks, which are too much under the horse, usually with a poor second thigh and cut-in above the hock.

Cow Hocks.   If viewed from the rear, the points of the hocks come together and the toes turn out. Such a horse is liable to brush.

Bowed Hocks.   If viewed from behind, the points of the hocks are wide apart, the toes turn in and the foot is likely to screw as it comes to the ground.

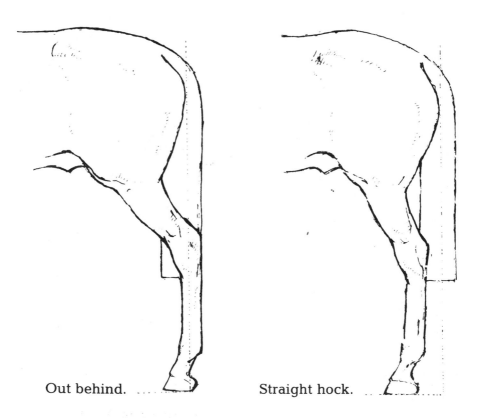

Out behind.   Straight hock.

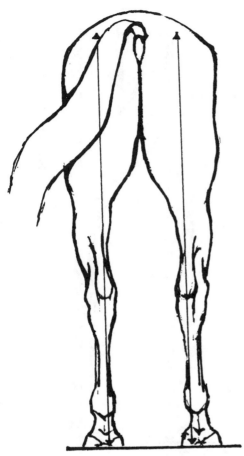

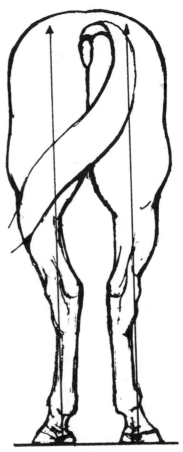

Split up behind.   Cow hock.

Straight Hocks. These are good for galloping, but have less leverage for jumping. There is more concussion unless compensated for by a long pastern. They are liable to strain, and young horses with straight hocks often suffer from a slipped stifle joint. This is usually rectified as the horse matures and the muscles and ligaments strengthen.

'Hocks in the Next County'. When viewed from the side, such hocks are way out behind the horse. There

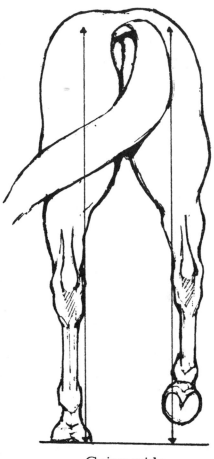

Going wide.

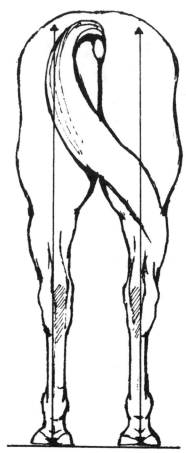

Good hocks.

is a big angle above the hock over the hamstring. Such horses often jump well, but rarely gallop.

Developing an Eye for a Horse

It takes considerable experience and constant practice to 'develop an eye' and to be able correctly to assess a horse's conformation. It can only be achieved by looking at many different types and sizes of horses, and by learning mentally to compare and evaluate what has been seen.

ASSESSING CONFORMATION

First look at the horse at rest in the stable. Then ask the attendant to bring out the horse and stand it up for inspection.

General Impression
☐ Does everything match?
☐ Assess the size of head in relation to body, and parts of the body in relation to each other.
☐ Consider the size of body in relation to the amount of 'bone' and to the length or shortness of legs.
☐ Assess structure and size of forehand in relation to hindquarters.
☐ Look at the size and shape of the feet.

Head, Neck, Forehand, Legs and Feet
☐ Check teeth for age, wolf teeth, and bit injuries.
☐ Check shape of the upper and lower jaw, and width between the branches of the lower jaw.
☐ Check the set of the head on the neck.

Stand in front of the horse and check:
  Width of the chest.
  Straightness of the legs.
  Size and shape of the knees.

Stand on the left or near-side and:
  Check the shape and feel of the withers.
  View the angle and length of the shoulders.
  Check by eye and right hand the position and set of the elbow joint.

Face towards the tail and run the left hand down the back of the forearm, knees, tendons and fetlock joint of the left leg. Move to the right or off-side and compare the look and feel of the right leg.

Face the horse and:
>   View the size and shape of the knee, the cannon bone, fetlock joint and pastern.
>   Crouch down and using both hands check the front and back of the knee and leg to the coronet.

Face towards the tail, run the left hand down the shoulder and leg and pick up the foot. If necessary, pick out the foot. Check the size and shape of the foot, sole and frog. If the horse is shod, check the shoes for fit, type and wear.

Repeat above procedure with the right leg.

The Middle
Stand back and view the general outline:
>   Top line.
>   Length of back.
>   Depth of girth.
>   Shape of ribs.
>   Strength of loins.

Run your left hand over the withers and along the back. Then feel the ribs and loin area.

Feel for muscle development and condition.

The Hindquarters, Legs and Feet
Stand back and view the outline, particularly:
>   Length from hip joint to hock.
>   Stifle to hock.
>   Hock to fetlock.
>   The size and shape of the hock, and the angle at which it is set on.
>   The development of the muscles of the second thigh.

Run your hand along the body and over the quarters.

Take hold of the tail, and standing behind the horse check:

The levelness of the points of the hip, and the width between the points of the hip.

The muscular development of the buttocks and upper thighs.

The straightness of the hind leg from point of buttock through the hock joint to the ground.

The angle of the foot.

Standing to the side, run your hand down the quarters and with both hands examine the hock joint for signs of strain or injury.

Feel down the hind leg in the same way as for the front leg, particularly the inside of the fetlock joint.

Check the hind feet in the same way as the front feet.

Repeat the last three procedures with the other leg.

Standing in front of the horse, look through the front legs and, diagonally, at the inner outline of the hock. Compare the outline of each hock joint.

ASSESSING CONDITION

Consider

The general impression, from expression of eyes and appearance of skin, coat and colour of gums. A running nose or eyes should be noted and mentioned.

The feel of the coat and skin. Staring coat and tight skin imply worms and lack of condition.

The feel of the horse's body:

Neck. Crest should feel tough and strong. Poor crest means no reserves of fat.

27

Back and Ribs. These should be well covered. In old age or pregnancy the weight of belly may give an impression of poorness above it. A second feel along the backbone should verify condition.

Quarters. Their shape varies according to breed and type. A fit horse has firm, well-developed muscles. A fat horse will show a round outline. A poor horse shows poverty lines down the back of the quarters, and the muscles will feel underdeveloped and soft.

The Feet. These reflect general condition and management. The outward evidence of changes – either for the better or worse – may take nine to eighteen months to show.

CHAPTER 2
Action

The ability of a horse to move well greatly depends on his conformation, breeding and type. A good mover uses himself equally well in front and behind.

To move well in front, a horse must use his shoulders as well as his knees and fetlock joints, actively. He should move straight, with a length of stride suitable to his make and shape. He should flow, giving an impression of moving with ease, which will be more

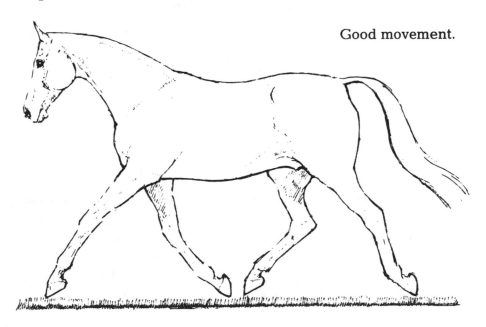

Good movement.

29

likely if the elbow is well positioned, allowing plenty of room between elbow and ribs. There should be slight knee elevation, but if this is exaggerated the horse may be better suited to driving rather than riding. A horse with an upright shoulder rarely moves well: he has a short stride and is a moderate ride. A show horse should always move straight.

The movement of the hind leg is equally important. Good movement comes from well-developed loins, quarters and thighs, and from active hocks. The appearance should be of strength and power. The action should again be straight, with the hocks brought well forward underneath the body.

In trot, if as the horse moves away from you he is sound and has full use of his joints, it should be possible to see the whole sole of each foot when the foot is at its highest point.

Some allowance should be made for young horses, particularly when trotted in-hand, and for four-year-olds when ridden. Lack of balance and muscular development may affect their action. As the horse matures and comes off his forehand, small defects in his action often disappear. A skilled farrier can do much to improve a horse's movement.

DEFECTIVE ACTION

Dishing

The front foot is thrown outwards, particularly in trot, and although this action appears to come from below the knee it is related to the flexion of the elbow. When still, the horse will often stand with toes turned in: 'pin-toed'. The movement can occur in one or both front legs. As long as it is only moderate dishing it is of little detriment to the horse, except for

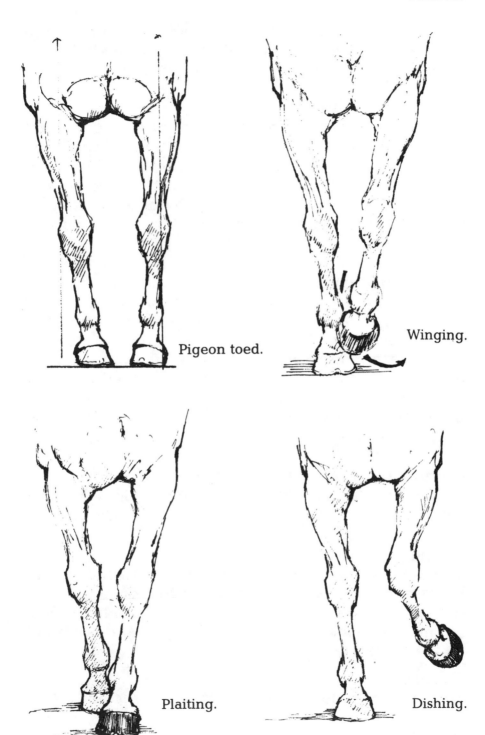

Pigeon toed.

Winging.

Plaiting.

Dishing.

31

showing. An exaggerated movement puts great strain on the fetlock joints, and this may eventually cause unsoundness.

Plaiting or Lacing
At walk and trot the horse places one foot in front of the other. This can apply to one or both feet. Narrow-chested horses are prone to this. Excessive plaiting is likely to make the horse stumble and even fall. A slight deviation can be acceptable. The knee should be carefully checked for any scarring or bruising.

Toes Turned Out
Horses who stand with either front or hind feet pointing outwards usually brush their legs, knocking the inside of their fetlock joint with the opposite foot. Evidence of this is an enlarged joint from constant bruising and/or rubbing off of the hair over the joint. It is a serious fault, as it necessitates always using protective boots when the horse is ridden, which can cause other problems.

Going Wide Behind
This often relates to stiffness in the back, and the hind legs are frequently bowed outwards. It is unsightly.

Forging
This is not considered to be a defect, as usually it can be corrected. It occurs in trot when the toe of the hind shoe strikes the underneath surface of the front shoe on the same side. The front foot lingers and is caught by the back shoe.

Causes:
Free-moving young horse, not yet sufficiently bal-

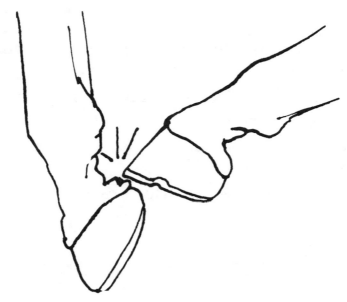

Overreach – usually occurs when jumping or galloping in deep going

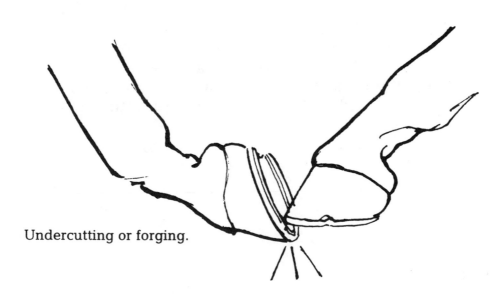

Undercutting or forging.

anced and strong under the weight of the rider, thus not able to bring the weight off the forehand. The problem ceases when the horse is stronger and better balanced.

Trotting too fast. This is usually the rider's fault. If the trot is slowed down the forging ceases.

Poor conformation. The remedy is schooling to improve and build up muscles.

Feet too long at the toe, which can be corrected by a farrier.

ASSESSING ACTION AND SOUNDNESS

☐ Ask the attendant to walk the horse away, turn and walk back. Check on evenness, and length of stride and head movement.

☐ Ask the attendant to trot the horse away, turn and trot back, keeping to as straight a line as possible. Check on the straightness of movement, the activity and levelness of the trot, the evenness of the movement of the horse's head.

☐ Ask for the horse to be trotted up again, and view from the side. Observe the general attitude of the horse.

CHAPTER 3
The Psychology of the Horse

When dealing with horses and ponies it is important to bear in mind their natural lifestyle and their instinctive defences. For many centuries they were nomadic, grass-eating, herd animals, and speed was their greatest protection against enemies. Even a newly-born foal was soon on its feet, ready to keep up with his mother and, if the necessity arose, to join the rest of the herd in flight. Bucking was an instinctive, defence reaction to dislodge a predator leaping on the back. Thus, if a horse is frightened, his first thought is to gallop off, bucking as he goes.

If a frightened horse is cornered, his instinct is to kick his way out. He may also stamp and strike out with his front feet. Allied with this protection behaviour is a very acute hearing, good eyesight – both forwards and to the side – and a nose sensitive to any strange or foreign smell. Horses therefore react very quickly should anything disturb or alarm them. Their first thought is flight; if this is made impossible they resist and fight. It is essential that on these occasions any person dealing with the horse is of a calm temperament and unafraid.

Horses have little reasoning power but excellent memories. Their training from the earliest age must establish confidence, trust, and good habits which in time become instinctive. Their memory can, however, also work against them. If startled or frightened by circumstances or people, a horse never forgets. Given the same situation he will always be likely to think back and react in a similar way.

Most bad behaviour by horses, both in and out of the stable, is caused by incorrect handling, particularly when the horse is young. The horse is a creature of habit, and appreciates a regular routine. He can be easily upset by sudden and unexpected change.

Frequent Problems and Possible Causes

Pulling back when tied up.
Cause: Tying up before the horse is calm. Tying up too short, so that the horse feels restricted.

Kicking or biting when being groomed.
Cause: Nervous groom, sensitive skin, rough handling.

Bad to shoe.
Cause: Insufficient handling of feet when young. Hasty or rough farrier.

Bad to box.
Cause: Hasty or rough handling, insufficient time taken to box. Frightening the horse by driving too fast, particularly on corners.

Kicking when travelling.
Cause: Insufficient room to balance, resulting in restriction and fear.

Pulling back when in trailer.
Cause: Tying up before back strap and back are put up.

Resisting examination and treatment.
Cause: Fear, pain, nervous handler.

The Herd Instinct

This is exhibited in the following ways:

Young horses often show unwillingness to leave others or reluctance to work alone.

Horses left on their own when others are taken away will often gallop about, and may even jump over a fence or gate.

A group of horses or ponies in a field will usually have a herd leader and a very distinctive pecking order. This is very obvious when hay is fed loose on the ground in winter.

As the herd instinct is very strong it can be used to help control and manage horses in such instances as:

When horses are stabled they are always happier and more settled if other horses are within sight and hearing.

When travelling, a young or nervous horse often settles if allowed a quiet old pony as a travelling companion.

Horses at grass are happier when in company. Ponies who are difficult to catch will often give in if encouraged to follow others to the gate.

A horse who gets loose away from his stable or field feels insecure and worried and tends to return to familiar surroundings. He usually goes back to either the stable or outside the field gate.

CHAPTER 4

Teeth and Ageing

The horse has three types of teeth. These are (1) molars or grinding teeth, (2) the incisors or biting teeth, and (3) the tushes. The *molars* are situated to the rear of the mouth, on either side of the face and in the upper and lower jaws. The *incisors* are in the upper and lower jaws in the front of the mouth. The *tushes* are found in the space between the other two groups of teeth. To open the mouth safely the fingers may be inserted into this space – which is where the bit lies.

The horse grows two sets of teeth during his lifetime: temporary milk or deciduous teeth and permanent teeth. The temporary teeth are small and white with a distinct neck. Permanent teeth are larger, stronger, pale fawn or yellow in colour, with no distinct neck.

TYPES AND NUMBER OF TEETH

Molars or Grinding Teeth
These are in the long head bones and jaw bones. Their function is to grind the food. There are twelve

temporary molars; three in each upper and lower jaw. There are twenty-four permanent molars; six in each upper and lower jaw. The molar teeth – due to the criss-cross movement of the jaws as the horse eats – wear unevenly and may require regular rasping to maintain a level surface. It is the outside of the upper teeth and the underside of the lower teeth which will need attention. If the sharp edges are left, mastication is affected, and the horse may also cut the inside of his mouth.

Incisor or Biting Teeth
These form a rather flat arch in the front of the top jaw or maxilla, and in the front of the lower jaw, the mandible. Their function is to cut through growing herbage and to collect food. There are twelve temporary incisors and twelve permanent incisors, six in each jaw. The centre teeth are called 'centrals', on either side of them are the 'laterals' and the remaining ones are called 'corner' teeth.

Tushes
These are found in the mouths of adult male horses. They appear between the incisor and molar teeth, one in each jaw, four in all. They appear at the age of three-and-a-half to four years, and are fully developed twelve months later. They were originally 'weapons', but now serve no purpose in the mouth of the domesticated horse. If awkwardly placed, they can sometimes cause discomfort when a bit is in the mouth. As the horse grows older they often become encrusted with tartar, which should be removed to prevent the gum from becoming inflamed. Tushes can be present in the mouth of mares, but they are small and often barely show through the gum.

Wolf Teeth

These are small extra teeth usually found only in the upper jaw, close up against the first molar tooth. They may be of varying size and root depth, but are always smaller than the true molar. They are usually discarded with the milk teeth. There are occasions when they remain in the jaw and cause the horse considerable discomfort when bitted. Their presence often goes unnoticed, and they can be the cause of mouth problems.

It is almost always advisable to have wolf teeth removed by your veterinary surgeon. This should be a simple task, but occasionally may require surgery if deep roots are encountered.

Before starting to train young horses or retrain older horses their mouths should be inspected in case of teeth problems. When inspecting the mouth, always untie the horse. Most horses will show some resentment when having their mouths looked at, so a tactful approach is needed.

THE PARTS OF THE TEETH

The surface of the tooth which bites and/or grinds the food is called the *table* or contact surface; it is this which gets worn down.

The *crown* of the tooth is that part which is above the gum. In milk teeth, the point where gum and tooth meet is the *neck*.

The *root* part of the tooth lies within the jaw. It is hollow and its cavity contains the blood vessels and nerves which nourish the tooth.

As the incisor tooth grows older, this cavity, the *fang hole*, fills up with a substance of a lighter colour. As the table of the tooth wears down, this will eventually appear as a small white area on the centre of the tooth in front of the mark.

The **mark** or ***infundibulum*** is the blackened depression seen on the table of the permanent incisors. It is lined by a ring of enamel. In the young tooth the mark is broad and deep, but as the table of the tooth wears down, the mark becomes shallower and eventually disappears. The blackening of the mark is due to discolouration from food and is not present in the new tooth.

TEETHING

When new teeth are coming through, the horse's gums become inflamed and painful, and if on feed other than grass they may make eating uncomfortable. Such animals should be put on a soft diet and meadow hay. Ridden horses can become more sensitive in their mouths, and if the problem is not recognised this 'mouthiness' can turn into a permanent habit. Horses should not have a bit in their mouths until the teeth are through and the gum healed, so the mouths of all young horses should be regularly checked, particularly when they are likely to be cutting teeth. Should there be any unusual tooth formation or wolf teeth present, veterinary advice should be sought.

AGEING THE HORSE

The official age of Thoroughbred and warm-blood horses is taken from 1 January.

The age of a horse can be assessed by inspection of his incisor teeth. This assessment can be reasonably accurate up to the age of eight years. After this,

41

changes are visible, both in the shape of the teeth and the tables, but the time of their occurrence varies among different horses, largely according to their management and diet. Experienced observation of many different horses enables an approximate opinion to be given. When offering this opinion, consideration should be given to all aspects of the mouth and teeth.

MILK TEETH

Birth or shortly after	Two central incisors appear in each jaw.
4–6 weeks	Lateral incisors appear.
9–10 months	Corner incisors appear.
12 months	All incisor teeth are in full wear.
2 years	Incisor teeth show signs of wear.

Inexperienced people may mistake a two-year-old mouth for that of a five- or six-year-old. Both mouths will have a full set of incisor teeth, but the teeth of a two-year-old are smaller and whiter. The molar teeth of a two-year-old consist of three temporary molars and two permanent molars in each jaw. The five-year-old has six molars in each jaw. A five-year-old male horse will have a fully grown tush.

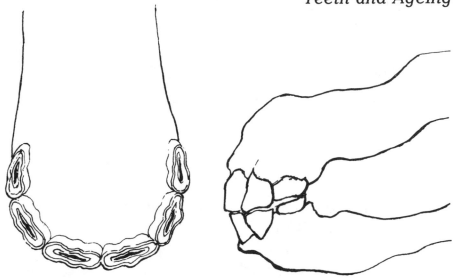

2 years. Milk teeth are whiter than permanents.

2½ years. Permanent centrals erupt.

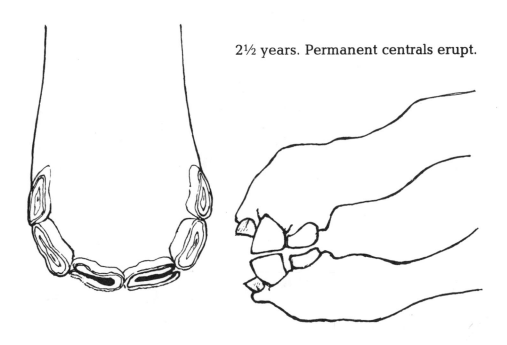

PERMANENT TEETH

2½ years   The central milk teeth are gradually replaced by the permanent incisors which at **3 years** are in full wear.

3½ years   The lateral permanent incisor appears and at **4 years** are in full wear.

4½ years   The corner incisors appear and in the male, the tush.

5 years   The corner incisors are well up but smaller than their neighbours. The tables are not quite level or in full wear. The tush is well grown.

6 years   The corner incisors are in full wear but the 'mark' is less distinct.

Looked at from the side, the teeth meet approximately at a right angle. From now on changes appear on the tables, first of the central incisors, followed by the lateral and then the corner incisors. Changes in the mouths of undershot or overshot horses do not necessarily follow the normal pattern.

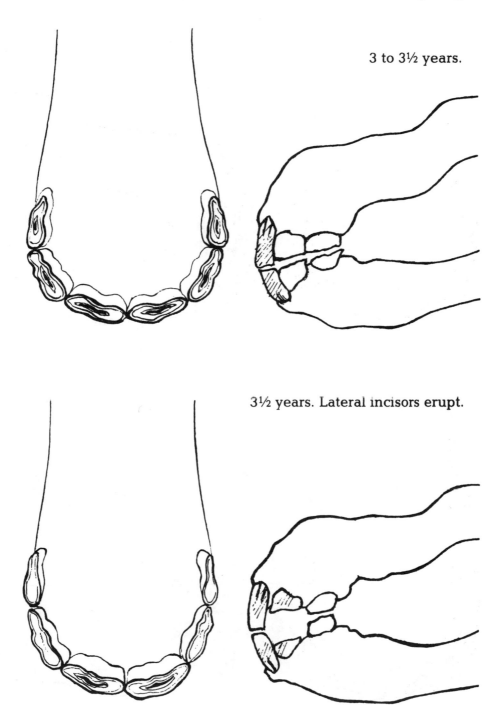

3 to 3½ years.

3½ years. Lateral incisors erupt.

45

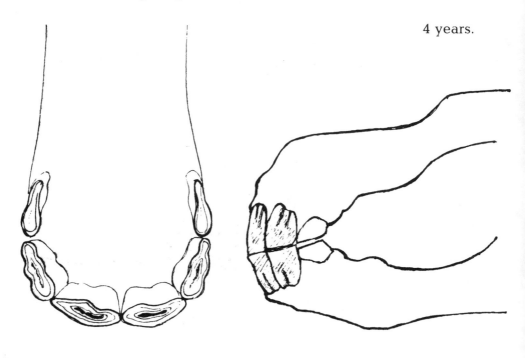

4 years.

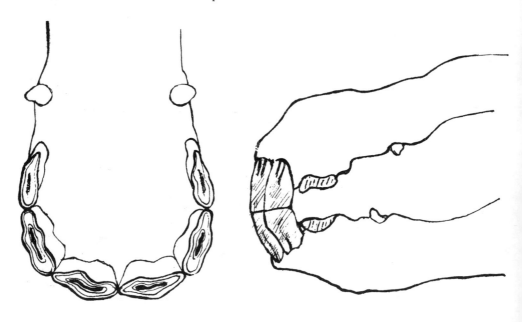

4½ years. Tushes are uncommon in mares.

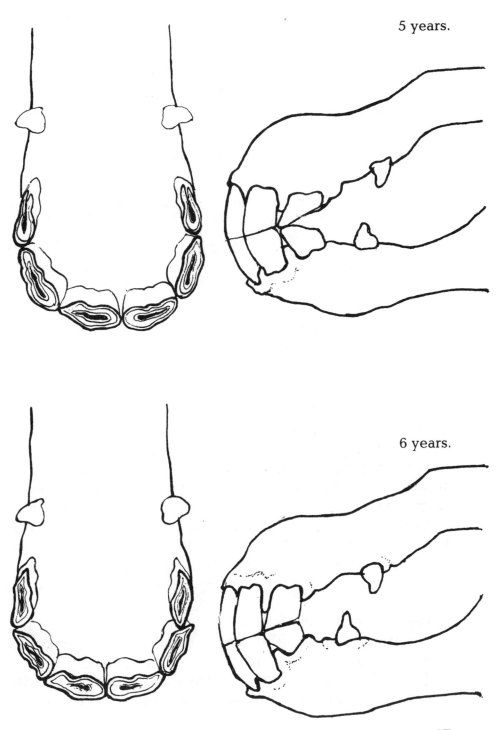

5 years.

6 years.

7 years	The mark on the central incisors may have gone, and that on the lateral incisors may be less obvious. A distinct hook shows on the edge of the upper corner incisor: the 'seven-year hook'.
8 years	The mark may have disappeared from the lateral incisors and is less distinct on the corn incisors. The seven-year hook has been worn level. The fang hole or 'dental star' is seen in the central incisors as a line in front of the mark.
9 years	The mark has gone from all incisors. The dental star appears on the lateral incisors.
10–12 years	The dental star gradually becomes a spot rather than a line and is present in all incisors.

Galvayne's Groove

This is a depression on the outer side of the upper corner incisor. It is seen mainly in cold-blood heavy horses. It is often absent in warm-blood light horses or ponies. It appears just below the gum at nine to ten years, has grown half way down by fifteen years, and to the bottom by twenty years. It is half grown out at the top by twenty-five years and disappears at thirty years.

Eleven-Year Hook

Although this normally appears at eleven years, it can appear any time from nine years on. By reference to the tables and the length and shape of the teeth, it should be possible to distinguish it from the

7 years.

8 years.

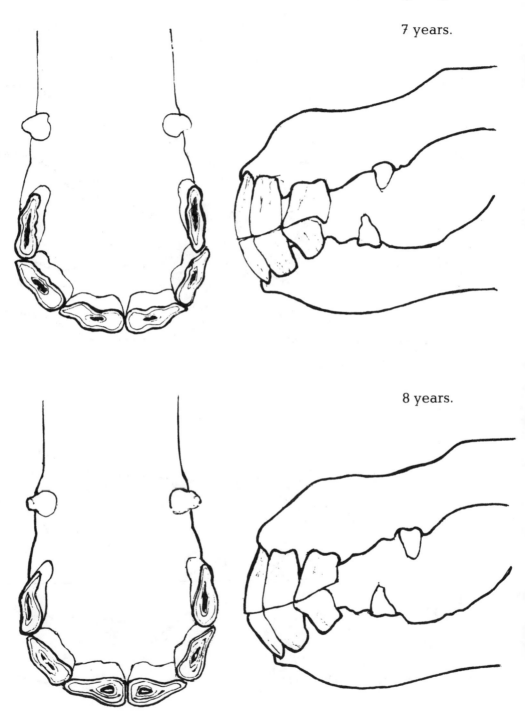

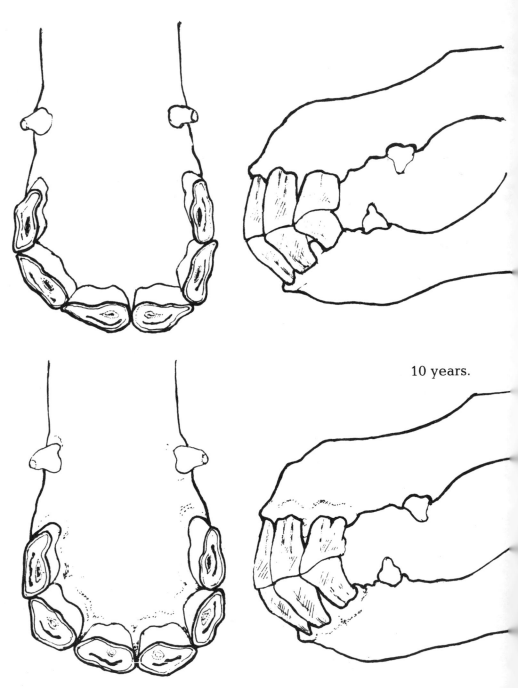

9 years.

10 years.

50

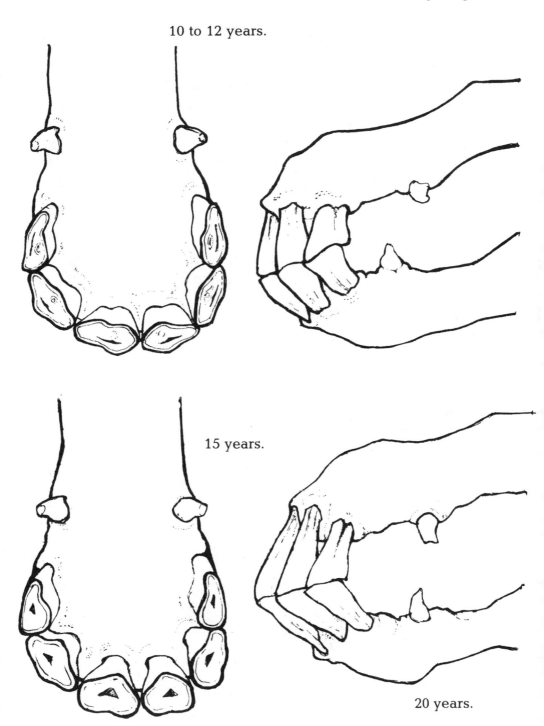

10 to 12 years.

15 years.

20 years.

seven-year hook. It usually persists throughout the remainder of the horse's life.

Shape of the Table and Angle of the Teeth

From the age of seven years onward, the tables of the teeth will change from oval to round and then to triangular. The back of the tooth forms the apex of the triangle. As the horse ages, his gums recede, his teeth appear to be longer and they project more forward and at a more acute angle.

Bishoping

This is the practice of attempting to make an old mouth look young. The teeth are filed short, and a false mark is gouged out of the centre of the table. The practice can be recognised, as the teeth do not meet naturally, and there is no enamel lining to the false mark.

Crib Biting

When examining a horse for age it is easy to recognise signs of crib biting. The central, and possibly lateral, upper teeth are worn on their outer edges.

CHAPTER 5

Breeds

Breed societies keep a stud register. For a horse or pony to be recognised as belonging to a certain breed and to be recorded in the Stud Book of that breed society they must be qualified.

Most breed societies are affiliated to the British Horse Society. An up-to-date list can be found in the current *Horseman's Year Book* published by the British Horse Society.

The following are some of the well-known breeds:

Thoroughbred
The word Thoroughbred is used to describe horses registered in the General Stud Book, which was first published in 1791 and is generally referred to as the GSB. All these horses can trace their ancestry in the male line to three Arab stallions imported into Britain in the late seventeenth and early eighteenth centuries: the Byerley Turk, the Darley Arabian and the Godolphin Arabian. On the female side, all horses in the GSB trace back to some thirty mares, mostly of Arab blood, originally bred or imported by King Charles II in the early seventeenth century and known as 'Royal Mares'.

The accepted abbreviation for Thoroughbred is TB.

Messrs Weatherby of Wellingborough, Northampton-shire, keep the *General Stud Book*, and TB types are registered by reference to them. Foals should be entered before they are four months old. The information required is sex, age, colour and markings, name of the previous owner and/or breeder and the sire and dam.

Since 1974 Weatherby's have kept a *Non-Thorough-bred Register*, previously published by Miss F.M. Prior as the *HB* (half-bred) *Stud Book*. Up to 1987 this was for the produce of TB stallions out of mares who had been identified by Weatherby's. Entry has now been widened to include the produce of certain non-TB stallions registered with Weatherby's.

HIS Mare Register This is a register kept by the National Light Horse Breeding Society (NLHBS), open to the stock of stallions approved by the National Stallion Association. This society runs a scheme whereby selected stallions are sent to various districts, and are available for use by owners of both TB mares and mares of other breeds. The stud fee for members is subsidised by the Society, which thus makes the services of a valuable stallion available to many more owners of mares. All selected stallions are judged and examined at an annual show.

British Warm-Blood

This is a new breed group started in the 1970s. The foundation stock are the Continental warm-bloods (Hanoverian, Danish Warm-Blood, Dutch WarmBlood etc.), many of which have been mated with the Thoroughbreds in Britain. Mares and stallions are eligible for the Stud Book on the basis of pedigree, plus conformation, action and veterinary tests. The aim is to produce a British Warm-Blood with correct conformation, athletic movement and a tractable temperament, which is particularly suitable for dressage, jumping and general riding.

Arab
The Arab is a foundation breed, crossing with which has improved other breeds of horses. Many countries now have their own Arab breed societies and stud books. In the United Kingdom the Arab Horse Society produces three stud books:

For pure-bred Arabs.

For Anglo-Arabs – a cross between Arabs and Thoroughbreds.

For part-bred Arabs – horses having a minimum of 25% Arab blood crossed with any breed other than Thoroughbred.

Cleveland Bay
This is a breed of great antiquity originating in Yorkshire. It has been used mostly as a carriage horse, and with the revival of driving is still popular. It is also in demand as a show jumper, eventer and hunter.

Irish Draught
This breed has been used in Ireland as a general farm horse. A stud book was started in 1917, and in the 1970s steps were taken to maintain the breed which, because of the popularity of its cross-bred, was diminishing in numbers. When mated with Thoroughbred or Arab blood the mares produce quality weight-carrying stock, which has achieved great success in competitive sports and as hunters.

Hackney
The Hackney horse is descended from the Norfolk Roadster, which until the mid-19th century was used as a general utility animal on farms in the eastern counties. The first stud book was published in 1883.

The modern Hackney, or Hackney Pony, ranges in height from 13-15.3hh (145-155cm). It has a fast and spectacular trotting gait, with good use of the shoulders and great flexion and thrust from the hock.

The Hackney is now mostly seen in the show ring and in driving competitions. It can be a bouncy riding horse.

MOUNTAIN AND MOORLAND BREEDS

Nine of these breeds are indigenous to the British Isles. Many of the smaller breeds have some Arab blood whereas large ponies such as the Dales were crossed with Clydesdale to give the offspring greater size and strength.

The severity of the native environment has made the breeds very hardy. For many centuries they have had to survive in winter with the minimum of food and shelter, which has ensured that only the toughest of them have been left to carry on the breed.

The popularity of trekking holidays has increased the demand for the larger ponies and cobs. They make admirable mounts for novice adults, and are capable of carrying heavy riders.

Welsh
There are five types of ponies and cobs registered with the Welsh Pony and Cob Society:

Section A   is the *Welsh Mountain Pony*, the foundation stock of all the other sections. The ponies make excellent mounts for children, and have been very successful in the show ring. They have also been used to improve many other breeds. They are well-made, pretty ponies with good movement. They should not exceed 12hh (122cms). Grey is the dominant colour, but all colours except piebald and skewbald are accepted.

Section B is the *Welsh Pony up to 13.2hh (134cms).* This pony has more bone and substance than the Welsh Mountain Pony. Colour as for Section A.

Section C is the *Welsh Pony cob type over 12hh (122cms) not exceeding 13.2hh (134cms).* This pony is an excellent ride and drive type. Colour as for Section A.

Section D is the *Welsh Cob.* There is no height limit, but 15hh (152cms) is favoured. This is a general utility animal, which makes an excellent riding or driving horse and is a good jumper. It has been crossed very successfully with other breeds to give greater substance and stamina. When crossed with suitable Thoroughbred stock it has produced successful dressage horses, show jumpers and driving horses. Colour as for Section A, but excessive white markings are not popular.

Section E consists of *geldings only.* Heights are as for the Sections above, except Section D cobs, where height is unlimited.

Connemara
This pony breed originated in western Eire, and there are now numerous private studs in England. It makes

an excellent mount for a teenager or a light adult, and is known for its good temperament and jumping ability. A Connemara crossed Thoroughbred makes a good all-round competition horse. The pure-bred stands 13-14.2hh (132-144cms). The predominant colour is grey. There are also blacks, bays, browns and various shades of dun, some verging on palomino.

New Forest
These ponies have bred in the New Forest for many centuries. There are now many private studs, where selective breeding has improved the stock. They make a good type of riding pony, ranging in height from about 12-14.2hh (122-144cms). They can be any colour except piebald, skewbald or blue-eyed cream. They have an equable temperament and are easy to train. Crossed with TB or Arab blood they make excellent small riding horses of great versatility.

Dartmoor
These ponies are indigenous to Dartmoor. They breed wild on the moor but are also bred privately off the moor. They make good children's ponies and are also used successfully for private driving turnouts. In height they should not exceed 12.2hh (127cms). They are usually brown, bay or black. White markings are discouraged. Piebald or skewbald colouring is barred. They make good foundation stock and, when crossed with other breeds such as TB or Arab, have produced many successful show animals.

Exmoor
These ponies have bred on Exmoor for centuries. They are distinguished by their heavy mane, 'mealy'

nose and 'toad' (i.e. hooded) eyes. They are about 12.2hh (124cms) in height, and are bay, brown or dun in colour, with 'mealy' shading under the belly and inside the forearms and legs. There should be no white markings or white hairs. They make good riding ponies for children, but need careful training. They are also capable of carrying a small adult.

They are now bred off the moor, but the moor pony is still the foundation stock. Exmoors can always be identified by brand marks, which are given when the pony is examined as a foal by Exmoor Pony Society inspectors. If of suitable standard, the pony is allocated a number which is branded on the near flank; the Exmoor star and the herd number are then branded on the near shoulder. Most unbranded ponies bred on the moor are not of true Exmoor stock.

Dales
These ponies are native to North-Eastern England. They are a well-built cob-type of animal, with active paces suited to driving. In height they should not exceed 14.2hh (144cms). In colour they should be black, brown, bay or grey, with limited white markings. The local term 'Heckberry Brown' means a deep chestnut with black dapples on the coat. They grow a considerable amount of fine 'feather' on the legs and heels. They are quiet docile ponies, much favoured for trekking.

Fell
This breed is smaller than its neighbour the Dales, and is not over 14hh (141cms). It is bred on the western side of the Pennines. It is strongly built, active, and brown or black in colour. It makes an excellent ride

and drive pony of cob type. White markings are discouraged. Broken colours or chestnut are barred.

Highland
The Highland pony is a breed of great antiquity. There were three types ranging in height from 12.2-14.2hh (124-144cms), but cross-breeding has merged the differences. Well built and sure footed, they were originally used on small highland farms and for carrying deer. They make good docile riding ponies, and the larger ones are capable of carrying adults. In colour, grey and various shades of dun predominate. There should be no white markings.

Shetland
These ponies originated in the Shetland Isles, where many are still bred. They are a very ancient breed, exceptionally strong for their size, and should not exceed 42ins (106.6cms). In former years they were employed as pit ponies. They are now used very successfully for driving. Their small height also makes them popular as riding ponies for children – although they are wide and can be strong, requiring firm handling. There are no limitations as to colour.

Cross-breds
The pure-breds do not fulfil all the demands of riders or drivers, and in Britain there has been considerable cross-breeding to produce cobs, hacks, hunters and show jumpers. As mentioned above, the mountain and moorland breeds, particularly the Welsh Cob and Connemara, are popular for this purpose.

Heavy Horse Breeds
These are also used for cross-breeding. Many good

heavyweight riding horses are produced by putting a Shire or Clydesdale mare to a TB horse. If Percheron or Suffolk Punch mares are used, the offspring grow less feather on the legs. The Percheron cross tends to have the better action.

DESCRIPTIVE TERMS

Half-bred. Denotes a horse of whom one parent is a Thoroughbred.

Threequarter-bred. Denotes that one parent is a Thoroughbred and the other a half-bred. These animals can now be registered.

Type. These include hunters, hacks, polo ponies, cobs and vanners. They are usually cross-breds, and are distinguished from breeds as they are not registered in a stud book.

Cold-Blood. Applies to heavy work-horses such as Shires, Clydesdales and Percherons.

Hot-Blood or Full-Blood. Applies to Eastern breeds: i.e. Arab, Barbs, etc, and to Thoroughbreds.

Warm-Blood. Applies to horses with a mixture of blood in their foundation stock. These breeds are used for riding and driving.

Pony. The difference between a horse and a pony lies more in build and movement than in exact height, but a show pony should not exceed 14.2hh (144cms).

Breeds

Horse. A horse is generally described as 15hh (152 cms) and over, but any animal over 14.2hh (144cms) may be deemed a horse.

Arabs. Whatever their size are always referred to as a horse.

Hack. A lightweight horse of TB type. Show hacks range from 14.2-15.3hh (144-155cms).

Cob. A sturdy weight-carrying type not exceeding 15.3hh (155cms).

Hunter. A type and usually a half- or threequarter-bred animal, ranging from 15.3hh (155cms) upwards.

Polo Pony. A TB type under 16hh (162cms) with weight-carrying ability suitable for riders.

Mule. A cross between a donkey stallion and a pony mare (female horse).

Hinny. A cross between a horse stallion and a female donkey. The name 'Jennet' is also used to denote this cross.

CHAPTER 6

Breeding

MARES AND FOALS

Breeding a foal is an expensive and labour-intensive business and should not be undertaken without considerable thought and planning. Unless either the stallion or the mare have a proven record, it is unlikely that the breeder will make a profit on the eventual progeny, whether it is a small pony or a racehorse.

Considerations

Facilities
It is essential to provide safe facilities for rearing a foal. Good clean grazing of not less than three acres is required. 'Clean' means that it has not been grazed by horses with a worm burden; that is not 'horse sick' (*see Grassland Management*, Book 3). Ideally, it should have been cross-grazed by cattle or sheep during the previous twelve months. Fertilisers, if used, should be organic. There should be very safe fencing, as foals have little sense of self-preservation, and shelter should be available from the prevailing winds.

A loosebox or barn large enough to hold the mare

and foal is another requirement: 4.25 x 4.25m (14 x 14ft) is the minimum size for Thoroughbreds, but 4.6 x 4.6m (15 x 15ft) is more suitable. A smaller size is adequate for ponies.

Selection of Mare and Stallion

It is important to breed from tough, strong mares of good conformation, who are free from known hereditary disease, and who, if possible, have stood up to work. Consideration must be given as to the type of young horse required and, if it is to be sold, as to whether there is a market for it. It is pointless to breed a foal whom no one wants. Proven ability and soundness in both mare and stallion should be considered. The eligibility of the foal to obtain registration papers is becoming more important, so both parents should be registered or eligible to be registered with a society.

A stallion who complements the mare should be chosen. The *breed societies* have lists of the various stallions standing at stud. The *National Light Horse Breeding Society* runs a Premium Scheme which chooses selected Thoroughbred horses to stand at stud at reduced rates in most districts. The *British Warm-Blood Society* has a list of their graded stallions. The stallion should be seen and the quality of the stable management at the stud taken into consideration.

In many cases it is sensible to delay sending the mare for service until late April or May. The foal will then be bred in the warmer weather, and the fresh grass will encourage a good supply of milk from the mare. Foals destined to be shown in-hand are better born earlier, as they are more mature for the first shows.

MANAGEMENT OF THE MARE

Before Being Sent to the Stallion
The mare should be in good condition but not fat. She should be improving in condition rather than being let down.

She should have been wormed regularly, preferably at four- to six-week intervals.

She should have been immunised against, influenza within the last two months. Her tetanus vaccinations should be up to date.

She should have had her hind shoes removed (some studs prefer the front shoes to be removed as well).

Note should have been taken of the dates she came in season over the previous six weeks.

Most studs insist that mares are swabbed by a veterinary surgeon, and passed clean before they are served. This can be carried out at home, but some studs insist that it is done at the stud.

The stallion owner/stud groom should be informed of all the above facts. In addition, they should be told if she is a maiden or barren and – if she has previously had a foal – whether there were difficulties getting her in foal. If she is due to foal at the stud, details of the last date of service and anything known about her previous breeding history should be supplied.

She should be sent to the stud with:
- A well-fitting comfortable headcollar, preferably with her name or the owner's name on it.
- Her passport if she has one.

☐ Her 'flu and tetanus certificate if she has no passport.

☐ A veterinary certificate of cleanliness if she has been swabbed at home.

☐ A foal slip or headcollar if she is to foal at the stud.

At Stud

She may be out all the time or in at night. She is 'tried' (*see Breeding Glossary*) to determine whether she is coming in season. When she is ready, she is served by the stallion. She is 'tried' again two to three weeks later to see whether she has 'held' to the first service. Depending upon the arrangements made with her owner, she is returned home.

After Returning Home

☐ If she has not been tested 'in foal' at the stud, this has to be done (*see Pregnancy Tests page 00*).

☐ She should be kept in good condition, but not allowed to become too fat.

☐ She should be wormed regularly with a wormer which is safe for pregnant mares.

☐ She may be ridden gently for a few months if desired. Mares who look well and have shelter from the bad weather may remain out at grass until a short time before foaling. This type of programme is certainly best for mountain and moorland ponies.

☐ Stabled mares should be turned out as much as possible, but only with other mares or alone, not with colts or geldings. Most mares need to be brought in at night from November onwards, but should still be turned out for exercise during the day. If the fields are too wet, the mare should be allowed to go loose in an indoor or outdoor school.

☐ After September the grass becomes less nutritious, and extra feed should be given as required.

☐ Whether in at night or out all the time, as soon as the grass loses its feed value she should be fed good hay and 1.8-3.6kg (4-8lbs) of hard food. Ponies require less hard food. During the last months before foaling, the hard food needs to be increased (see below).

The Last Four Months Before Foaling
☐ The mare carries the foal for approximately eleven months, and during the last four months the foetus grows very fast, its size and weight increasing three-fold. A vitamin and mineral supplement is needed, and energy requirements should be gradually increased by about 12% over this time while the roughage intake is somewhat reduced.

☐ A month before she is due to foal she should have a tetanus booster. She should also have a 'flu innoculation, if this has not been done in the last six months. Antibodies are passed to the foal in the colostrum (*see Breeding Glossary*).

☐ The mare must continue to be regularly wormed. Worms are lethal to young foals, and can be passed in the mare's milk, or picked up by the foal eating the mare's droppings. It is important that the wormer is safe for pregnant mares, and that the instructions are carefully followed.

FOALING (Parturition)

The mare carries the foal for between 320 and 350 days. The average is about 335 days.

If the person in charge of the mare is experienced, and if assistance is available, the mare can be foaled at home. If not, and especially if the mare is valuable and has been to an expensive stallion, it is safer to send her to a recommended stud to foal. If she is to be put in foal again she can go to the stud where the stallion stands.

Foaling Away From Home

It is better to send the mare at least three weeks before the expected foaling date, so that the upsets of the journey do not bring on the foaling, and she can settle down and acquire some immunity to the germs at the stud.

Foaling at Home

Facilities

☐ A large, safe, disinfected loosebox with as few fittings as possible. A good size is 4.6m x 4.6m (15ft x 15ft).

☐ A deep, clean straw bed, well banked up on the walls.

☐ Good lighting.

☐ Some means of viewing the mare without disturbing her.

☐ A safe available power point, which can be used if necessary for heating.

Parturition.

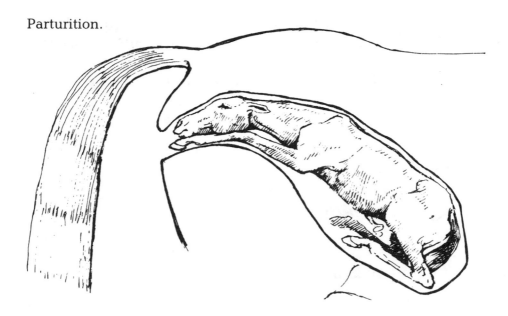

If she is foaling at home and is the only in-foal mare, it is better for her to sleep in the foaling box a week or two before the expected foaling date.

Signs of Foaling

Bagging Up. During the last few days the udder grows larger, stiffer and rounder. During this time the udder may be gently handled, so that the mare does not resent being suckled. This is particularly beneficial with maiden mares.

Waxing. Usually between six and forty-eight hours before foaling starts, the teats exude a wax-like substance. This is not a reliable sign, as it may be closer to the foaling or the mare may not wax at all.

Slackening. The muscles on either side of the root of the tail slacken; this occurs usually twelve to eighteen hours before foaling.

Breeding

When Foaling is Imminent.   It is wise to put a light, well-fitting headcollar and a clean tail bandage on the mare.

The likely signs, which may be spread over a period of about four hours, are:

Walking the box.

Pawing bedding.

Looking round at flanks.

Kicking at the belly.

Swishing the tail.

Lying down and getting up again.

Starting to sweat.

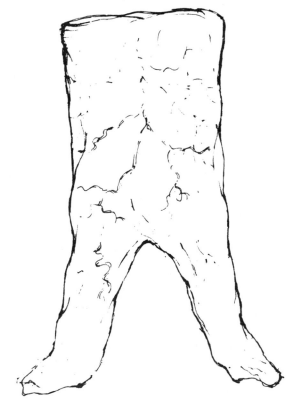

Placenta.

At this time she should be watched constantly, but without disturbing her. At night, the lights should be left switched on.

The veterinary surgeon's telephone number and an antibiotic powder for the foal's navel should be at hand.

The assistant's hands should be well scrubbed before handling the foal or mare.

Normal Foaling

Usually, but not always, the mare lies down.

1. The foetal fluids are discharged as the bag breaks. The foal should then be born within ten to twenty minutes.

2. Within about five minutes, the front legs appear, still inside the membrane, with one foot slightly in advance of the other.

3. The head appears, lying along the front legs.

4. The shoulders appear, and then the mare usually has a short rest.

5. The membrane over the nostrils (caul) should break. It is essential that this is done before the navel cord is broken, otherwise the foal suffocates. If the foal has not broken this for himself, the watcher may do so, but not until the foal's ribs are clear of the mare.

6. The hind legs slip out, or may be withdrawn by the foal.

7. The foal may struggle to get up, or the mare may get up and the cord will be broken naturally. The

watcher can then sprinkle antibiotic powder over the stump.

After the first discharge (Stage 1 above), the foal has only one to three hours to live inside the mare. If there is any deviation from the sequence just described, veterinary help should be sought immediately. The vet requires hot water, soap and clean towels.

After Foaling

If all has gone well, which in the majority of cases it does, the mare and foal should be allowed to rest, but should be watched unobtrusively. Usually within an hour the foal is on his feet and trying to suckle. It is very important for him to get this early milk (colostrum – *see Breeding Glossary*), as it contains the antibodies which protect him for the first few months of his life. After that time he starts to manufacture his own.

Some foals are very slow to find their way to the udder and have to be helped.

Sometimes a maiden mare resents the foal and has to be restrained. The assistant can hold up a front leg; a tranquilliser may be given; or in very severe cases the mare can be twitched. As the application of the twitch can cause a rise in blood pressure, care must be taken. It is possible to cause a haemorrhage in a newly-foaled mare.

Sometimes the foal does not get up. This may be because the cord has broken early, and the foal has not obtained a full blood supply. If he otherwise seems bright and healthy, two people may support him with a clean sack under his belly, so that he can get to the mare's udder. There are cases where it may be necessary to milk the mare and let the foal drink from a sterilised bottle with a calf's teat on the end. If the foal is not bright and alert, or begins to behave strangely, veterinary help should be sought immediately.

The afterbirth (*see Breeding Glossary*) gradually separates from the uterus and is expelled by the mare, often within an hour of foaling. If it is retained for more than three hours, veterinary help should be sought. On no account should any attempt be made to pull it away. It should be inspected to make sure that nothing has been retained inside the mare (see diagram).

As soon as the mare is on her feet, she should be offered a chilled drink and (if she will take them) electrolytes may be added. Hay may be given, and after an hour or two a small feed. Hay should always be fed loose, so that there is no danger of the foal becoming entangled in the net.

Foaling Outside

Advantages

It is nearer to nature.

There is less risk of infection.

Disadvantages

In an emergency it is difficult to provide human assistance, especially at night.

The mare may choose a dangerous place to foal: i.e. too near a fence.

In bad weather the foal may suffer.

Once the foal is on his feet the mare may refuse to be caught.

If this practice is to be followed, a safe, level, well-fenced field with no ditches, ponds or other hazards should be chosen. There should be no horses or cattle in the field and it should be adjacent to the stables. There should be some shelter: i.e. a thick hedge, or shed.

Usually the system works well with ponies, but for valuable horses it is not advisable.

The mare and foal should be caught and handled each day. In bad weather, driving rain, and wind, they should be brought in.

MANAGEMENT AFTER FOALING

The First Twenty-four Hours

Some people like their foals to have an antibiotic injection within the first twenty-four hours. In any case, it may be a wise percaution for the vet to check the mare, the foal, and the afterbirth. He can also check whether the meconium has been expelled correctly (*see Breeding Glossary*).

The mare and foal should be looked at frequently. The foal must be seen to be suckling successfully. He should pass the meconium, which is blackish and may be hard, within thirty-six hours. If this is not passed, veterinary assistance may be sought, or an experienced person can give an enema. The mare may remain on the same diet as before foaling – i.e., high protein mash-type feeds – but smaller quantities of energy food should be given for the first few days. It is unwise suddenly to introduce bran mashes, as the mare's digestion will not be used to bran. If she has been having flaked barley, mashes may be made from this.

After the First Twenty-four Hours

If the weather is good, the mare can be led out with the foal (*see Handling Foal* page 79) and given an hour's grazing. With an unknown mare it is wise to graze her in-hand the first time she goes out. She should have a headcollar on when she is turned loose with the foal. When the mare is released the foal should be in front of her, where she can see him, so that she will not kick him by mistake as she gallops off. The foal should be led out and not allowed to go loose. He should be released before the mare.

March foals should come in at night with their dams until the weather improves. As long as the weather is suitable, May foals (after they are one week old) can be left out at night, but they should be caught and handled daily.

When the flies become troublesome the mare and foal may be brought in during the daytime. They should also be brought in during bad weather. If a foal is very cold and shivery he should be rubbed down, and if possible put under a heat lamp. It is also wise to bring foals in before a thunderstorm, as horses shelter under trees and are therefore vulnerable to lightning. During storms young horses can panic and may gallop through fences.

Scouring

The foal is likely to scour when the mare first comes in season on the foaling heat. This is quite normal. However, should he start scouring at any other time, an antibiotic injection may be necessary to deal with any infection. Severe scouring can be serious owing to the danger of dehydration.

The foal's hindquarters should be kept clean by

washing and drying them carefully. Baby oil applied on either side of the tail can help to prevent the coat being lost.

Worming

Most modern wormers are safe for foals. The instructions should be carefully followed. Worming should be carried out as early as the product allows. Keeping foals as worm-free as possible is a vital safety measure. Much damage, if not death, can result from a worm burden and – even if not evident at the time – can result in serious trouble later in life. Many cases of colic and subsequent death are attributable to worm infestation when young.

The mare should be wormed at the same time as the foal. Thereafter it is sensible to worm them both every four weeks.

Feeding the Mare

Feeding the mare depends on the quantity and quality of the grass. In May and June, when on good grazing, no supplementary feeding may be necessary. At other times, or if on poor restricted grazing, the mare will need additional food to maintain her own condition and the milk supply for her foal. Quantities must vary according to circumstances, and a close watch should be kept on the condition of both mare and foal. The foal may or may not look thin and ribby when he is born, but should quickly start to look round and well. The mare's condition has no bearing on her foal's well-being. Very fat, good doers often make the worst mothers, both in producing a foal in good condition and in keeping it looking well.

When the grass is highest in protein and at its most digestible – i.e. in May and June – the diet must not be too high in protein. Before the grass starts to grow, and, again, when it starts to lose its value (after it has seeded) the protein/energy food should be increased.

If the mare is in foal again, this should be taken into consideration.

Specimen Daily Feed

During the winter and for the month before foaling

Best meadow hay *ad lib*.

1.8-3.6kgs (4-8lbs) oats, flaked barley or stud cubes or mixture.

0.45-1.8kg (1-4lbs) dry sugar beet soaked for twenty-four hours.

57gms (2oz) milk pellets or 113gms (¼lb) soya bean meal.

28gms (1oz) salt.

Calcium. Ground limestone or equivalent: 28gms (1oz). (This is particularly important on land with a low lime count.)

Additives. Selenium and vitamin E if the land is deficient in selenium.

Two weeks before foaling, you can, if you wish, begin to substitute flaked barley for part of the oat ration. The oats at this stage should be rolled and both they and the sugar beet may be made into mashes if required, both before and after foaling. Bran mashes should not be suddenly introduced.

March and April
As above.

May and June
Depending on the grazing, no supplementary feed at all or up to half of the above without milk or soya.

July onwards
Working gradually towards the March ration, but without milk or soya.

October onwards
As the grass begins to lose its value, dried milk or soya meal may be re-introduced to ensure that the essential protein content of the diet is maintained.

Feeding the Foal
Encourage him to eat some of the mare's rations by putting the food in two separate feed bowls.

Foals requiring extra food because they are not doing well should be fed by hand on a nutritious and easily digested diet.

Too high a protein diet causes the bones to grow too fast, and knuckling over may result, but foals require a higher protein diet than mature animals to enable them to grow. If too little calcium is fed, the end of the bones will not harden and epiphysitis may result.

Feeding the Weaned Foal
The object is not to allow the foal to go back in condition. Before being weaned he should be eating grass/hay and hard food. The constituents of the diet should not be changed but, if he has still been getting some milk from the mare, his food quantity should be stepped up.. Depending on his management during

the winter he may require more energy food as the weather deteriorates.

HANDLING THE FOAL

Foals should at all times be treated quietly but with firmness. The foal should be handled within twelve hours of his birth. Some foals are very friendly, others very shy.

To catch the foal, two people are required: one to hold and reassure the mare, the other to catch the foal. The foal may try to escape by going in front of or underneath the mare. He should be approached from behind, never from the front. He should be caught with one hand round the front of the chest and the other round the quarters. Once caught, he should be stroked and soothed. Within twenty-four hours, a foal slip should be fitted. An assistant to hold the foal makes this easier.

The Foal Slip or Headcollar
Opinion is divided as to whether the foal slip should be left on all the time. Many people consider this to be a dangerous practice, as it is easy for the foal to get caught up in it. Whether or not it is worn all the time it should be adjustable over the head and around the nose, and should be made of leather, not nylon, unless fitted with 'panic breaks'.

To put on the headcollar, fasten the headpiece round the neck first, push it forwards to behind the ears, and then fasten the noseband. To begin with it will need adjustment for length and tightness every three or four days. It must be carefully fitted, so that it is not too tight, but must never be loose enough for the foal to trap a hind leg when scratching his face. Each day the foal should be handled all over, and a hand run down his legs. After a few days his feet may be picked up.

Teaching to Lead

Leading lessons should start in the box. With a very young foal, put a stable rubber round his neck and move him along with a hand around his quarters. As soon as he understands this, a 1.8m (6ft) light rope may be threaded through the foal slip to guide and steady him, but a hand should be kept round his quarters to push him along and to prevent him running back, as he may fall over. The foal should be 'played' like a fish. The rope must be threaded through rather than clipped on, so that should he inadvertently escape, the rope will not be left dangling, which will frighten him.

Foals should not be allowed to go to and from the field loose; they may easily gallop into something and damage themselves. If the leading lessons are started early enough, they learn very quickly. If the training is left too long they become much stronger and, being unused to discipline, will be difficult to control.

When leading them out to the field, the mare should be in front with the foal close to her side. The person leading the mare should watch the foal, and stop immediately if he is left behind.

Feet

When the farrier comes to dress the mare's feet he should handle the foal and pick up his feet, even if they do not need attention. Foals handled only by women can become quite nervous with men. It is important to study the foal's action and to keep his feet correctly trimmed. This will prevent unlevelness of the foot caused by faulty action.

Weaning (see *Breeding Glossary*)
When deciding the best time to wean, several considerations must be taken into account. If the mare is not in foal again there is no hurry, and the foal may be left with the mare until she weans him naturally. If the mare is in foal again, the best time for weaning is usually when the foal is five to six months old.

For the last month, the foal should have had a companion, ideally another foal, or, failing that, a small, good-natured pony or worm-free donkey. The foal (and his companion) should be put in a box which he knows, and both the bottom and the top door should be shut. The mare should be removed to a safe place out of earshot of the foal. A box a mile away may be necessary. They should be kept apart until the mare's milk dries up and the foal begins to settle down. They should not be put near one another for at least four weeks.

After Weaning
The mare must be given a low protein diet and plenty of exercise. If she has a lot of milk, her bag should be examined carefully each day to make sure that she is not developing mastitis (see *Breeding Glossary*). It is not advisable to draw off the milk, as this encourages further production.

Pony foals may winter out as long as there is shelter, but young horses usually lose too much condition. The latter are best turned out in the daytime, and kept in at night. This means that they lie warm and dry without expending food to keep themselves warm, and they are able to take the daily exercise which is necessary to ensure that they grow up strong and active.

STALLIONS

Stallions who are used solely as stud horses have a rather different lifestyle from those who are ridden in equestrian activities, though some do both.

The annual programme for Thoroughbreds, or similar stallions, used solely for stud work begins three to four months before the start of the stud season. At this time, daily exercise must begin, so that the horses are fit before starting their duties. At Thoroughbred studs, mares are covered in February, but at other studs usually not before March.

After the season is over, which may be June, or even later, the stallions should be let down and roughed off. Stallions who are ridden as well as being used at stud, should have a particularly strict régime so that they understand what they are required to do in the differing circumstances. It is important to use a different bridle and to choose a special place for serving the mares.

When dealing with stallions, discipline is of paramount importance. Their natural pride and arrogance must not be spoiled, although they must understand that their handler is the boss.

When being attended to the horse should always be tied up. A chain, rather than a rope is essential, as stallions by their nature pick up everything with their teeth. People dealing with them should not wear scent or aftershave, as the smell is likely to 'rouse' them.

When holding or leading a stallion it is advisable to carry a stick or whip. If he is being led in a headcollar, a clip chain under the jaw or over the nose, attached to a long lead rope, is a sensible precaution. If he is being led in a bridle, a coupling to the bit and a lead rein 2.4-3.6m (8-12ft long) should be used. The attributes for dealing with all stallions are patience, firmness and common sense. There should be no fear and no loss of temper.

PREGNANCY TESTING

Manual. This is carried out by a veterinary surgeon, from thirty-five days after service up to the time of foaling. Some experienced vets can detect pregnancy earlier than this.

Blood Testing. This is carried out between forty-five and one hundred days after service. A blood sample is collected from the jugular vein and sent to a laboratory for analysis. The test is a biological one, for gonatrophic hormones.

Urine Testing. This is carried out at any time after 130 days. A urine sample is collected by the owner and sent to a laboratory to be tested for oestrogenic components.

Ultra-Sound Scanning. This method of testing is now available from most veterinary surgeons who special-ise in treating equine breeding stock. It can be used from seventeen to twenty days after the last service.

CHAPTER 7

Identification

Brand Marks

Brand marks are used to denote breed or ownership. A hot branding iron carrying the appropriate mark is applied to the horse's skin. Horses imported from Europe often carry a breed mark, which is usually found on the left hindquarter but can be on the shoulder and/or neck.

Many native ponies breeding wild on the hills and in the forests are branded, to denote ownership. A general round-up takes place in the autumn, and ponies in their first year and then still running with their mothers can be easily identified and branded. The brand is usually on the quarters, under the saddle, or on the shoulder.

Freeze-Marking

To deter thieves, many owners now have their horses freeze-marked. The process has been patented by Farm Key of Banbury, who keep a national register of horses, their owners, and their allocated numbers. The process is quite painless and leaves a permanent white identification mark. It is applied either under the saddle or under the mane.

To Describe a Horse Consider

Colour.

Sex.

Markings.

Height:

> With a measuring stick. (See below.)
> By eye or by touch. Use your own eyes, mouth or chin as a marker: e.g., for a 5ft 3in person the chin is about 14.2hh (147cms). Then stand up to the horse's wither to gauge the approximate height.

Age.
> See Chapter 3. Examine teeth: length, tables, shape and condition.

Type.
> Stand back and check build and bone shape.

Sex and Age
The word horse can be used to describe the whole equine species without reference to sex. The following terms are more precise descriptions:

Stallion/Entire.   An uncastrated male horse of any age.

Gelding.   A castrated male of any age.

Colt.   An uncastrated male under four years of age.

Mare.   A female horse of any age.

Filly.   A female under four years of age.

Foal.   Described either as a 'colt' or 'filly' foal and under one year old.

A Rig is a male horse from whom only one testicle has been removed, the other not having descended into the scrotum. The condition is often difficult to diagnose and may well escape a veterinary inspection. It can often be assumed from misbehaviour in company, or reactions when turned out with other mares and geldings. A rig is capable of putting a mare in foal. The condition can be rectified, but would probably involve a major operation. Rigs are not suitable mounts for children. If known at the time of a sale the condition must be declared. If established at a later date, the sale can be declared null and void.

Height

Horses are measured in hands (4ins) and in centimetres: 10.16cms are equal to one hand. Shetland ponies are measured in inches and centimetres.

The measurement is taken from the highest point of the withers in a perpendicular line to the ground. For accurate measurement, the following items and conditions are essential:

☐ A measuring stick with a spirit level on the cross bar.

☐ The horse should be standing on a smooth and level surface.

☐ The horse must stand squarely on all four feet. His head should be lowered so that the eyebrows are in line with the withers.

☐ The horse must be calm and must remain still. If he is tense he should be allowed fifteen to twenty minutes to get used to having the stick placed on the withers.

For the purposes of the Joint Measurement Scheme, the horse must be measured without shoes. For general purposes, the shoes – providing they are of normal weight – may remain on and 12mm ($\frac{1}{2}$in) are taken off the measured height.

Life measurement certificates are now obtainable. The horse must be six years of age or over, measured without shoes, and the measurement must be taken by a member of a special panel appointed by the Joint Measurement Scheme.

Correct height measurement is important:

It forms part of a correct description of the horse for sale.

It provides for correct division and sub-division of horses in showing and jumping classes, and in other competitive sports.

It serves as some indication of size when buying saddlery and clothing, although type and build are of equal importance.

Colours

For the purposes of identification, it is important for a horse's colour and marking to be described correctly. His precise colour can sometimes be difficult to determine, but reference to the colour of his 'points' – muzzle, eyelids, tips of the ears, legs and the mane and tail – should clarify the problem. The legs below the knee can be black or a darker version of the body, but they also may have white markings. A horse with no white markings is said to be *whole coloured*. When describing horses, any patches of white hair caused by pressure or injury should be noted. These are most likely to occur in the saddle and bridle area or on the legs. Scars should also be noted.

Identification

A *black horse* is black in colour with black points and a black muzzle.

A *brown horse* is dark brown in colour with black limbs, mane and tail.

A *dark bay* horse is mid-brown in colour with black limbs, mane and tail.

A *bright bay* horse is mahogany in colour with black limbs, mane and tail.

A *light bay horse* is a paler shade of brown, or pale mahogany, with black limbs, mane and tail.

A *bay-brown* is a horse where the predominating colour is brown, with bay muzzle and black points.

A *dark chestnut* is a rich red colour with matching points. He sometimes has small patches of black hair on the body. He may be whole coloured as in a Suffolk Punch, but is most likely to have white markings on his legs.

A *chestnut* is a paler version of the above and may have a flaxen mane and tail.

A *liver chestnut* is a darker shade verging on brown with darker points.

A *grey horse* is one with both black and white hair growing in the coat, with matching points and mane and tail. The skin is black.

Iron grey has predominantly black hairs and can appear nearly black.

Light grey has predominantly white hairs.

Flea-bitten grey has dark hair growing in speckles over the body.

A *dapple grey* has circles of black hair growing over the body.

NOTE: All grey horses become lighter with age, but are never described as white. On examination, the skin will be seen to be dark coloured.

A *white horse* is one whose skin is white or pale pink. The skin is lacking in pigmentation, and the coat is white. It is a very unusual condition.

A *blue dun* is a diluted black colour evenly distributed. The mane and tail are black. There may be a dorsal stripe. The skin is black.

A *yellow dun* horse varies from mouse colour to dark gold with black points. He may show a 'list', a dark line along the back bone. The skin is black.

A *palomino* varies from light cream to bright gold with similar coloured points, and lighter or silver coloured mane and tail.

A *cream horse* has a light cream coat verging to white in the muzzle area and legs. The muzzle is white. The skin lacks pigment. The eyes may also have a pinkish or bluish appearance.

A *roan* has a mixture of white and other colours growing in his coat. There is a tendency to get whiter with age.

Identification

A *strawberry roan* is white and red with similar points.

A *blue roan* is white and black with black points. The coat has a blue tinge.

A *red roan or a bay roan* is white and bay or bay-brown with black limbs, mane and tail.

A *chestnut roan or sorrel* is white and light chestnut with matching points. Mane and tail similar or chestnut in colour.

A *piebald* is a mixture of large irregular patches of black and white. The mane and tail may also be black and white.

A *skewbald* is a mixture of large irregular patches of white and any other colour or colours.

A *spotted* horse often has pink or mottled skin. It may have:

(a) *Leopard spot marking* when dark spots are distributed over a lighter background.

(b) *Blanket marking* when there are dark spots on the rump of a lighter coloured horse.

(c) *Snowflake marking* when white spots appear on a darker background.

An *Appaloosa* has a pink skin, a silky white or grey coat with darker coloured spots on the coat. These markings can include, leopard, blanket or snowflake markings.

Odd coloured horses are those whose body coat consists of large irregular patches of more than two colours, which may merge into each other at the edges.

Markings

The Head

A *star* is a white mark on the forehead. It can be further described as large, small, irregular etc.

A *stripe* is a narrow white marking down the face. It may be a continuation of a star, and can be further described as narrow, irregular, etc.

A *blaze* is a broad white marking extending from between the eyes and down the face over the nasal bones.

A *white face* is an exaggerated blaze. It extends over the whole of the forehead, front of the face and to the mouth.

A *snip* is a white mark between the nostrils. If extending to a right or left nostril it should be so described.

A *white upperlip and underlip* describes skin at the edges of the lips.

A *white muzzle* describes where white skin is found on both lips and up to nostrils.

A *wall eye* is one which shows a lack of colouring matter. It has a greyish-white or blue appearance. The sight is not affected.

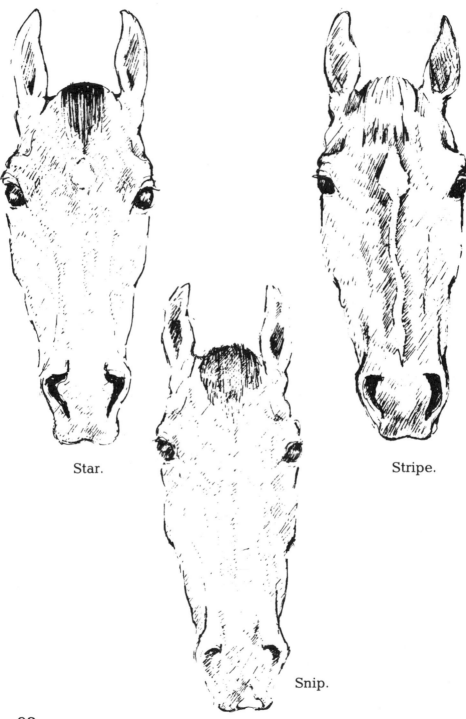

Star.

Stripe.

Snip.

Blaze.

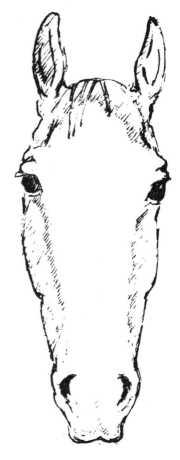

White face.

The Body

List, dorsal stripe and ray describe the dark lines along the back of dun horses. They are also found on donkeys.

Zebra marks describe any stripes on the body. They occur more frequently on donkeys.

Salmon marks are fine lines of white hair found on the loins and quarters.

93

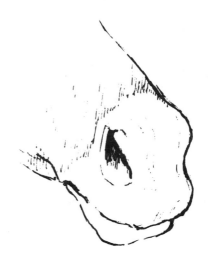

White muzzle.

White upper and lower lips.

White wall eye.

The prophet's thumb mark is a pronounced dimple sometimes found on the neck of Throughbred or Arab horses. It can also appear in the shoulder or hind quarters. It is said to be a sign of good luck.

Flesh marks are patches of skin devoid of colouring and care should be taken to use this term instead of white wherever appropriate.

The Legs

White markings on the legs are defined by reference to the anatomy. The traditional terms 'sock' or 'stocking' are now used only for casual description. Nowadays the terms 'right' and 'left' are used instead of 'off' and 'near'. For example, typical descriptions are: right pastern; left heel; right leg to above knee.

The term 'ermine' is used where black spots occur on white markings.

Hooves

Any variation in colour of the hooves should be noted, in particular a white stripe or line down the hoof.

Whorls

Whorls are formed by changes in the direction of hair growth. They are an established method of identifying horses, as they vary to some extent in every animal. They occur on the head, neck, body and upper limbs; when describing horses for identification it is the ones on the head and neck which should be noted. Grey and whole-coloured horses, or those with few markings, should have at least five whorls noted, either on the head, neck or body.

95

Identification

Sample description of a horse.

SAM

SIRE: Scottish Venture.
DAM: Breeding unknown.

Chestnut gelding. Foaled 1980. Height 16.1hh with shoes. Mane and tail on. Freeze-marked 6783 under saddle.

HEAD: Whorl in centre of forehead above eye level. Small star, narrow stripe and snip to left nostril.

LEFT FRONT: Small mark on front of coronet. White stripe on front of hoof. Whorl on postero-lateral mid-forearm.

RIGHT FRONT: Half cannon. White hoof.

LEFT HIND: Half pastern to mid-fetlock behind. White hoof.

RIGHT HIND: Threequarter cannon. White hoof.

BODY: Whorl left anterior crest. Whorl right mid-crest. Whorl left anterior jugular. Whorl mid-trachea.

ACQUIRED: Scattered saddle marks on both sides. Girth mark on left side. Scar anterior mid-cannon left hind.

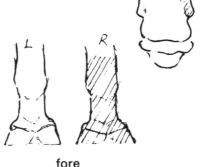

fore   hind

Chestnuts
For horses with fewer than five identifying whorls a print can be made of the chestnuts on each front leg. These are like human fingerprints and show a different shape and/or design in every horse.

Certification or Identity
Official certificates must be completed and signed by a veterinary surgeon.

Horses are identified by means of a written description of the horse and a sketch map of his body, together with separate sketches of the front view of the head, muzzle and legs. (See sample description, pp 96-97.)

White markings   on the horse should be outlined in red and filled in with diagonal red lines.

Whorls   are shown by an 'X' marked in black.

Scars   are shown by a tick marked in black.

White marks on a grey   are not noted except for flesh marks.

The written description of a horse must be in black ink, and should exactly describe the markings, whorls, and scars as shown on the sketch map. The description should start with the forehead.

The position of *head whorls* should be exactly described in relation to eye level, centre of forehead, and any white markings. *Crest whorls* on the neck should be divided into anterior, middle and posterior. *Body whorls* should be designated by reference to the particular anatomical position.

CHAPTER 8
Buying and Selling a Horse

BUYING

When looking at horses or ponies with a view to buying them, inexperienced persons should always take a more knowledgable person with them. Even experienced people find it helpful to have another opinion.

The owner of the horse should be asked to provide information as to age, any vices and/or bad habits, and suitability for intended use. It can be helpful if this information is written down in the presence of another unbiased person – who can, if necessary, corroborate what has been said.

If the horse is registered for competition, his record can be verified with the appropriate society. Breed papers should be available for inspection when the horse is first seen. If he is a show animal he may have a height certificate. If not, and if you intend to show him in height-restricted classes, the vendor can be asked to warrant the height.

Before coming to a final decision it is always advisable to have the animal examined by a veterinary surgeon – preferably one of the purchaser's own choice. Veterinary surgeons will not usually give a warranty as to soundness, and cannot certify height unless able to measure the animal under Joint Measurement Scheme rules. If they consider the animal suitable they will provide a certificate giving a description (including approximate height) and stating that the said animal has no abnormality or injury likely to affect his use for the purpose for which he is being bought. This certificate should be sufficient for insurance purposes. If possible, the intending purchaser should attend the vetting so that any queries can be answered on the spot. If this is not possible, it is certainly helpful to have a verbal report and to discuss the examination with the veterinary surgeon. Veterinary certificates can sometimes be difficult to interpret, especially for a layman.

Viewing the Horse

Procedure
First, insist on seeing the horse loose in his stable. Then have him brought out and stood still for inspection, before being walked and trotted up on a hard, level surface. Ask for the horse to be saddled up, and watch whilst this is being carried out. Ask for someone to ride and jump the horse before riding him yourself.

Remember, some horses will jump well over coloured fences, some will be bolder over natural fences, and some will perform very much better over known fences at home than they will over an unknown course. It is up to the purchaser to test the horse or to see it perform according to its proposed use.

Information Needed
According to intended use, it is advisable to obtain the following information about the horse in question:

☐ Is he good in traffic? This question should be

expanded to cover reactions to heavy traffic, high lorries, main roads, narrow side roads etc.

☐ Is he quiet to handle, groom, shoe, and clip?

☐ Is he good to box and travel, both in a trailer and horsebox?

☐ Is he free from any stables vices? These should be itemised. (See Book 2.)

☐ Is he well behaved in company: e.g. with hounds, other horses, dogs, children?

☐ Is he safe in a field with other horses, or happy to stay alone?

☐ Is he free from any known allergy?

☐ In the case of a child's pony or a horse for a novice rider, is he easy to catch, both on his own or in company, good to tack up, and well behaved on roads, particularly with regard to shying?

☐ In the case of a hunter it is a fair trial to be permitted to take him out hunting, or see him ridden out hunting. In this respect, make sure it is at the seller's risk.

☐ Young event horses should prove their willingness to go through or jump over water. Older horses can often be vouched for by independent testimony or by competition results.

Procedure After Deciding to Purchase
Confirm your decision in writing and keep a copy of your letter.

Agree to complete the sale at the stated price, subject to a satisfactory opinion from your veterinary surgeon. Should the veterinary surgeon give an unfavourable or qualified report, the buyer may still decide to buy, subject to an appropriate reduction in price.

List the information about the horse which has been supplied by the vendor.

State any agreed arrangements which will apply if the horse should prove unsuitable: i.e. return or exchange. (There may be no such arrangements.)

State that no responsibility is accepted for the horse until payment is made.

Confirm arrangements as to payment, and as to when the horse will be collected or accepted.

After payment for the horse, the buyer should take possession of the passport, breed papers and height certificate. The horse may have no official papers, but it is helpful to know records of 'flu and tetanus innoculations and worming programme.

The vendor may agree to this letter verbally, or he may write his acceptance, or he may ignore it. In any case, should the horse prove to be unsuitable the letter may help if the buyer wishes to return the horse and reclaim his money.

There are advantages in buying from reputable dealers, as they are usually willing to exchange a horse or pony should he prove to be unsuitable. With a private owner this is unlikely.

In most cases the buyer should remember the rule of common law *caveat emptor* – let the buyer beware. In the event of problems, the *Trades Description Act* and/or the *Sale of Goods Act* may apply. Legal advice will clarify this and its relevance, as the situation can differ according to whether the vendor is a dealer or private owner.

SELLING

The vendor can protect his interests in the following ways:

On meeting the buyer and seeing the horse ridden, he should indicate if he considers that the horse is not suitable.

He may state that he believes the horse sound, but should not declare him sound. This is a matter for a veterinary surgeon.

He should state the time limit that he will allow:
For trial.
To arrange the veterinary examination.
To come to a decision.

If paid by cheque he should ensure that the cheque is cleared or guaranteed before allowing the buyer to take possession.

He should state clearly that possession passes when the cash/cheque is paid, and that the buyer is responsible for the horse from that time.

A Trial
From a seller's point of view, this is rarely a sensible procedure. Should any accident or illness befall the animal, the question of responsibility is always a problem. It is wiser to allow the purchaser to make several visits, but not to take the horse home. If necessary, the horse can be taken to an independent yard and tried in new surroundings and over unfamiliar jumps.

If other buyers are interested, the purchaser must be given a definite time limit in which to decide.

AUCTION SALES

When buying or selling a horse or pony at an auction, both the purchaser and vendor are normally bound by the 'Contract of Sale Conditions' as laid down by the auctioneers in their catalogue. All prospective purchasers are advised to study these conditions before bidding in the sale. It is advisable for the seller or his agent to ensure that any statements made about the horse – or information given to the auctioneer to facilitate the sale of the horse – are true and demonstrable. Should the animal concerned fail in respect of some part of the information given by the seller, the purchaser may be entitled to return the animal to the seller, and to have his money refunded. Auctioneers usually retain any monies paid for at least twenty-four hours, and they should be informed immediately of any breach of sale conditions.

Should the purchaser suspect that pain-killing drugs have been administered to the horse (the analgesic effect usually wears off in twenty-four hours but may take up to fourteen days), he should inform the auctioneer and arrange to have the animal's blood tested.

ALLERGIES

Because of prevalence of '*allergic coughing*' it is essential to obtain information about the general management, feed and bedding of any intended purchase.

Head shaking or '*summer asthma*' is another allergy which may escape veterinary detection in the winter months. The animal does not exhibit the tell-tale signs until a spell of warm humid weather occurs. He will then wave his head up and down and strike at his face with a foreleg. There is no known cure for this ailment. At best, the horse will be uncomfortable to ride, and depressing to compete on, particularly in dressage; at worst he will be dangerous.

Sweet Itch is another summer complaint which can go undetected in the winter, particularly if the mane is hogged.

Laminitis is not an allergy but is a very common cause of unsoundness, particularly in ponies. It is a recurring disease which if diagnosed in its early stages can, with careful management, be avoided or controlled. Confirmed sufferers are easily diagnosed by changes in the shape of their feet. However, a mild attack may leave no visible evidence, although the tendency to recur will remain.

Blood Testing

As pain-killing drugs can be used to disguise un-soundness, many buyers and their veterinary sur-geons now ask for a blood test before a sale is agreed. There can be no valid objection to this from the seller, provided that all expenses are paid by the purchaser, and that the testing is completed without delay and in a proper manner.

X-Rays

In recent years it has become common practice for purchasers of valuable horses to ask to have the horse's feet x-rayed. In some cases they will ask for the leg and the knee or hock joint to be included. A foot x-ray can be a wise precaution. Other, more extensive, x-rays are justified if there is an old injury which needs investigation.

Many sellers are reluctant to have their horses x-rayed. Should the sale of the horse fall through because of the results of an x-ray, the seller is put in a difficult position with regard to future purchasers. Often an x-ray will reveal old injuries, many of which may never cause unsoundness. Also, a reasonable assessment can only be made by someone who has had considerable practice and experience in the actual reading of radiographs (x-ray plates).

Glossary

TERMS RELATING TO CONFORMATION AND ACTION

AGED
: A horse of eight years or over.

BACK AT THE KNEE
: See 'Calf Knee'

BEARING
: The alteration of the surface of teeth to disguise age.

BOLD EYE
: A prominent eye. Denotes a bold character.

BONE
: The measurement of the circumference of the bone and tendons immediately below the knee.

BOTH LEGS OUT OF THE SAME HOLE
: A narrow-chested horse whose legs are too close together, and are liable to move close and brush.

BOWED HOCKS
: The hocks are positioned outwards, the toes are turned in. These hocks are weak.

BOXY FEET
: Narrow, upright feet with contracted heels.

BROKEN KNEES
: Knees permanently scarred by injury.

BULL NECK	A short, thick neck which makes flexion difficult.
CALF KNEE	When looked at from the side, the knee slopes backwards, showing a concave appearance. There is little depth of knee from front to rear. The cannon bone appears to slope forward. There is too little room for attachment of tendons and ligaments. This is also referred to as 'back at the knee' or 'stag knees'.
CLEAN LEGS	Free from blemishes.
CLOSE COUPLED	A horse with a short back, strong loin, and well ribbed up.
COCK THROTTLED	Showing a very acute angle between head and neck. The head is carried high.
COLD BACK	A horse with a sensitive back. He often plays up or bucks when first mounted. This can be due to discomfort and/or pain. A numnah will help, as will saddling in good time before mounting, to allow the back to warm up.
COLT	Ungelded male horse up to four years old.
CONDITION	State of health and body: i.e. good, poor.
COW HOCKS	Hocks which turn inwards, while toes turn outwards. This is a weakness.

COW KICK	A forward kick with the hind leg.
CRESTY	Thick, convex neck, as seen in stallions.
CURBY HOCKS	Hocks with an enlarged area over the seat of curb, or of a shape likely to encourage the formation of a curb.
DAISY CUTTING	Smooth, low action at walk and trot, with much shoulder movement and little bending of the knee.
DEEP THROUGH THE GIRTH	Denotes plenty of heart room, well-sprung ribs, and deep from withers to elbow.
DIPPED BACK	Pronounced dip between withers and croup, which is usually a sign of age. In a young horse it is a sign of weakness.
DISH FACE	A concave line to the front of the face, often found in Arabs.
DISHING	The horse does not move straight but swings his forelegs outwards.
DOCKING	The amputation of the lower part of the tail. It has been illegal in Britain since 1948.
DONKEY FEET	Upright, narrow feet with contracted heels. See *Boxy Feet*.
DORSAL STRIPE	Continuous black, brown or dun stripe from the withers to the tail. Also called 'eel stripe' or 'list'.

EWE NECK	The top line of the neck is concave rather than convex. The neck is 'upside down' or badly put on.
FALSE CURB	A bony enlargement at the head of the splint bone. This is not detrimental, and should not be mistaken for a true curb.
FALSE NOSTRIL	This is found at the top end of the nostril, in the shape of a small pocket. See *High Blowing*.
FALSE RIBS	The last pairs of ten ribs are bound together by cartilage, and are not attached at their lower end to the sternum.
FAVOURING A LEG	When moving, the horse avoids putting his full weight on one front leg. This is a sign of discomfort or lameness. See *Pointing*.
FEATHER	Long hair on the fetlocks and legs found in cart horses and some native ponies. A sign of common blood.
FIDDLE HEAD	A large, ugly head.
FLAT BONE	Relates to the satisfactory look and feel of the cannon bone, which should never give an impression of roundness or puffiness.
FLAT SIDED	The ribs are not well sprung. Also known as 'slat' or 'slat sided'.

FLOATING RIB

This is the last rib of the false ribs, and is not attached by cartilage to the previous rib. See *False Ribs*.

FORGING

The hind shoe strikes the front shoe when trotting. This is common in free-moving young horses when first ridden. As balance improves, it should not occur.

GIRTH PLACE

This position is just behind the elbows. The sternum or breast bone curves up slightly to allow room for the girth.

GONE IN THE WIND

Old-fashioned expression which covers respiratory unsoundness and bronchitis.

GOOD DOER

A horse which always looks in good condition, even on a moderate food ration.

GOOD FRONT AND GOOD LENGTH OF REIN

A horse with a well set-on, sloping shoulder and good length of neck. The saddle sits well into the back.

GOOD HUNTER

A warranty in these two words implies soundness in wind, eyes and action. Quiet to ride and capable of being hunted.

GOOSE RUMPED

The top of the croup has an obvious bump and is prominent, with a more acute slope to the quarters. It is of no detriment and often goes with jumping ability.

GRASS BELLY — A large stomach typical in horses resting at grass.

GUMMY OR GAMMY LEGS — The tendons and ligaments in the leg below the knee are hidden by the legs being puffy and filled. This is a sign of excessive hard work or strain.

HEAVY TOP — Coarse neck, shoulders and body, which are out of proportion to an otherwise light-framed horse.

HERRING GUTTED — The body runs up sharply from the girth to flanks, so that there is little depth at the flanks. Such horses are usually poor doers.

HIGH ACTION OR CLIMBING — This occurs particularly in front and at the gallop. The body is lifted unnecessarily high off the ground at each stride. Speed and stamina are affected.

HIGH BLOWING — A noise heard when some horses are galloping. As the horse breathes out, the movement of air flaps the false nostril. It is not a sign of unsoundness.

HOBDAYED — Describes a horse who has had an operation on the larynx to relieve whistling. Named after Professor Sir Frederick Hobday, the first veterinary surgeon to practise it.

HOCKS IN THE NEXT COUNTY — Hocks which are set well be-behind the line of the quarters.

HOCKS WELL LET DOWN	Implies good length from point of hip to hock, and short cannon bones, so that the hocks are comparatively close to the ground.
HOLLOW BACK	Excessively dipped back, which gives a weak but comfortable ride. A horse with this back is suitable only for light-weight work.
IN-HAND	A horse which is led. Show classes are 'ridden' or 'in-hand'.
JUMPING BUMP	See *Goose Rumped*.
KNEE ACTION	Pronounced movement of the knee, as seen in driving ponies and cobs. The stride is often short.
LACING	See *Plaiting*.
LIGHT OF BONE	The measurement below the knee is small and not large enough to support the body of the horse easily.
LOADED SHOULDER	Thick, heavy shoulder with a low wither. The horse with this has a poor gallop.
MAKE A NOISE	When the horse canters, gallops – and sometimes even trots – he 'makes a noise'. This is caused by an unsoundness of wind.
MARK	The dark centre of a tooth of a horse under eight years. If there are no marks, the horse is over eight years old.

MULE	The offspring of a male ass and a female horse.
NAIL BIND	Caused when the farrier drives a nail too close to the sensitive laminae. If not withdrawn it will cause lameness.
NARROW BEHIND	The croup and thighs lack muscle.
NARROW IN FRONT	With insufficient room for heart and lungs. The forelegs are likely to brush.
ON THE LEG	Long in the leg in comparison to the body. Too much space between ground and belly.
OPEN KNEE	Indentation at the front of the knee. It shows a weakness in the bony structure of the knee.
OVER AT THE KNEE	The knees appear to have a convex outline and the cannons slope to the rear. It is of little or no detriment.
PARROT MOUTH	A malformation of the upper jaw. The top incisor teeth overhang the lower teeth. Biting grass may be difficult, but chewing is not affected.
PAST MARK OF MOUTH	An aged horse over eight years.
PEACOCKY	A high head-carriage often allied with an upright shoulder.
PIG EYE	A small, mean eye.
PIGEON TOES	Front feet which turn inwards.
PIN TOED	The front feet turn out and are likely to brush.

PLAITING	The front feet cross over each other when the horse is moving, so that he is likely to stumble.
POINTING	This occurs when a horse is still and takes the weight off a front leg, placing it forward. It is a sign of discomfort in the leg, foot, or back.
POOR DOER	A horse which is difficult to keep in good condition, in spite of good food and care.
POVERTY LINE	A line down the back of the quarters caused by lack of flesh and muscle.
PROPHET'S THUMB MARK	A dimple found on the neck.
QUIDDING	The dropping of food out of the mouth when eating. It is usually a sign of tooth trouble.
QUITTER OR QUITTOR	A fistulous sore at the coronet.
RAGGED HIPS	Prominent hip points, wide apart. They can be a sign of strength.
RISING	A term used when ageing horses. A horse of four years eight months would be described as rising five. Five off is a horse just over five.
ROACH BACK OR HOG BACK	The horse's back has a convex outline.
ROARER	A horse when galloping makes a loud roaring noise. It is an affection of the larynx.

115

ROMAN NOSE	A nose with a convex outline.
RUNNING UP LIGHT	The appearance of a fit horse after a strenuous effort: i.e. after a race, an Event, or a long day's hunting. The line of the belly runs sharply up from the girth line to the flanks.
SHELLY FEET	Brittle and thin-soled feet.
SHORT	Going short means that the front action is restricted suggesting discomfort and on-coming lameness.
SHORT OF A RIB OR SLACK OF A RIB	Too much space between the last rib and the point of hip.
SHORT OF BONE	Too small a measurement of bone, according to the type of horse.
SHOWING WEAR	A reference to rounded and thickened fetlock joints.
SICKLE HOCKS	Bent and weak-looking hocks. When on the ground, the foot is in front of the hock.
SPLIT UP BEHIND	The quarters viewed from behind are short of muscle in the upper thigh, and there is a large gap between the hind legs. The horse is usually a poor doer.
SPRUNG HOCK	Swelling and heat over the seat of curb.
STANDING OVER	An appearance of giving at the knee. This is not detrimental, unless caused by overwork.

STANDING OVER A
  LOT OF GROUND
A horse with a good sloping shoulder, a short back, and a long croup.

STANDING UP A
  HORSE TO VIEW
Positioning a horse for a judge or perhaps a buyer to view.

STARING COAT
The coat is dull and does not lie flat. A sign of poor condition, worms, and possibly illness.

STRAIGHT MOVER
A horse which, viewed from in front or from behind, moves his limbs straight forward.

STRAIGHT SHOULDER
  OR UPRIGHT
  SHOULDER
An acute angle between the humerus and the scapula.

SWALLOWING
  TONGUE
A misnomer for the condition which occurs when a horse suddenly slows down and appears to choke. It is caused by a reaction from the 'soft palate' and is not connected with the tongue.

SWAN NECK
Long, thin neck with a tendency to 'ewe neck'. It is caused by over-developed muscle at poll and underneath the neck.

SWAY BACKED
A horse with an injured back behind the saddle. He usually finds it difficult to carry a rider.

THICK IN THE WIND
The horse makes a noise when breathing in. It can be a temporary condition which clears as the horse becomes fit. Or it can be a sign of unsoundness in the wind.

TIED IN AT THE ELBOW	The elbow lies so close to the ribs that it restricts the shoulder and forearm movement.
TIED IN BELOW THE KNEE	The measurement immediately below the knee is less than the measurement further down the cannon bone, resulting in insufficient room for tendons and ligaments.
TUBED HORSE	A roarer who has had a tube inserted in his windpipe approximately halfway down, through which he breathes.
UNDERSHOT	The lower jaw projects beyond the upper jaw. The bite, and therefore grazing ability, is affected.
UNNERVED OR DE-NERVED	The nerve supply to the foot is partially or entirely severed, by an operation, which can make a horse with foot lameness usable. This is now rarely performed.
UNSEEN	A term applied to horses bought on a written or verbal description.
WELL LAID BACK	Can apply to withers or the shoulder blade. It implies a long, sloping shoulder and a well-developed wither.
WELL LET DOWN	A well-developed hind leg with good shaped hocks and short cannon bones.
WELL RIBBED UP	A minimal gap between last rib and point of hip.

WELL SPRUNG	The ribs behind the girth give an impression of roundness.
WHISTLING	A noise made by a horse as he inhales. It is an unsoundness.
WIDE BEHIND	The hind legs are set wide apart and the horse moves with them in this position.
WOBBLER	A young horse, often a foal, affected with paralysis of the hindquarters. At present it is incurable.
ZEBRA MARKS	Stripe marks on the limbs, neck, withers, and quarters.

TERMS RELATING TO BREEDING

AFTERBIRTH	Consists of the foetal membranes, which are expelled after the foal is born.
ALLANTOIS	Part of the foetal membranes.
AMNION OR CAUL	The innermost of the three membranes which contain the foetus within the mare's body.
AMNIOTIC FLUID	The fluid which surrounds and protects the foetus.
BAGGING UP	The mare's udder begins to fill up with milk.
BARREN	The term applied to a mare who in spite of being served is not in foal.

Glossary

BREECH PRESENTATION	During parturition, the foal is presented with the quarters first, instead of the front feet. Immediate veterinary attention is required if the foal is to be born alive.
CASLICK'S OPERATION	Stitching the top of the vulva to prevent air and germs gaining entry.
CASTRATION	The 'gelding' of colts who are not to be kept as stallions, by removing the testes. This may be done as early as four months, or may be left until the colt is one or two years old.
CAUL	See *Amnion*.
C.E.M.	Contagious equine metritis. A serious venereal disease resulting in sterility.
CHORION	The outermost of the three foetal membranes.
COLOSTRUM	The first milk which contains the antibodies to enable the foal to resist infection. It is very rich in protein and in vitamins A and D. It is a laxative. After thirty to thirty-six hours the milk loses the antibodies and gradually becomes normal.
COVERING (MATING SERVICE)	The mare is served by the stallion, usually on the third and fifth days after coming in season.

EMBRYO	This is formed when the ovum and sperm unite and is so called until the various parts of the foal are visibly recognisable.
FOALING HEAT	This occurs when the mare comes in season for the first time after the birth of her foal, usually between six to nine days.
FOETAL FLUID	See *Amniotic Fluid*.
FOETUS	The fully formed embryo growing within the uterus. In the last four months before parturition it increases three-fold in size.
GELDING	The castration of a colt, or the name given to a castrated male horse.
GESTATION	The period of time during which the mare carries the foal. From 335 to 340 days is the normal time.
MAIDEN	A mare who has not previously had a foal.
MASTITIS	An infection of the udder. It may occur if the foal dies or when the foal is weaned. The udder becomes hard and inflamed, and the mare runs a temperature. The milk has hard lumps in it and may be discoloured.
MECONIUM	The foetal dung.
METRITIS	An infection of the uterus.

OESTRUS (IN SEASON; IN USE)	Mares come in season about every twenty-three days during the spring and summer. Good food, longer daylight and warmth all help to bring the mare 'on'. Oestrus lasts six to eight days in the spring, but decreases in summer.
PARTURITION	The act of birth.
PLACENTA	One of the membranes which surround the foal in the mare's uterus. It is connected to the foetus by the umbilical cord.
SERVICE	The act of covering a mare.
SLACKENING	The relaxing of the muscles on either side of the root of the tail, which occurs before foaling.
STITCHING UP	See *Caslick's Operation*.
SWABBING	This is done when the mare is in season, to ensure that she is 'clean': i.e. has no disease which could be transmitted to the stallion.
TEASER	Instead of using a valuable stallion to try the mare (see *Trying*), a less valuable stallion, or even a pony, is used.
TRYING	The mare and stallion are brought together to see if the mare is in season.
TRYING BOARD	A solid fence or filled-in gate over which the stallion is allowed to touch and nuzzle the mare to see if she is in season.

USE   See *Oestrus*.

UTERUS (WOMB)   A 'Y'-shaped, hollow, muscular organ. It consists of a body and two small horns.

WAXING   This occurs six to forty-eight hours before foaling, when the mare's teats exude a wax-like substance.

WEANING   The process of taking the foal away from his mother, generally when the foal is between five and six months old. If they are not separated, mares wean their own foals, usually at about eight months.

Bibliography

BRITISH HORSE SOCIETY, *Manual of Horsemanship*.

CODRINGTON, LT. COL., MRCVS, *Know Your Horse* (J.A. Allen).

MILLER, WILLIAM C., *Care and management of Thoroughbred Studs* (TBA).

ROYAL COLLEGE OF VETERINARY SURGEONS, *Colours and Markings of Horses*.

SMYTHE, R.H., MRCVS, *The Horse: Structure and Movement* (J.A. Allen).

SPOONER, GLENDA, *The Handbook of Showing* (J.A. Allen).

SUMMERHAYS, R.S., *Encyclopaedia for Horsemen* (Threshold Books).

Breed pamphlets.

Index

Index

Index